SAFE START

**An introduction to
health and safety
on construction sites**

SAFETY
HANDBOOK

Name _____

Company _____

GE 707

Published by the
Construction Industry Training Board
Bircham Newton, King's Lynn,
Norfolk PE31 6RH

First published 1990
Revised 1996
Revised 1999
New edition 2005
ISBN-10: 1-85751-109-3
ISBN-13: 978-1-85751-109-3
© Construction Industry Training Board 1990, 2005

2005 edition:

Written by Denis Hands MIOSH, RSP
Contributions by Gordon Eagle FIOSH, RSP
Copy edited by Gavin Fidler
Cartoons by Steve Chadburn
Signs provided by Stocksigns Ltd

The Construction Industry Training Board (CITB) has made
every effort to ensure that the information contained in
this publication is accurate. It should be used as guidance
material and not as a replacement for current regulations or
existing standards.

Printed in the UK

Contents

Introduction

The purpose of this book is to give you practical advice on:

- your responsibilities for looking after your own health and safety at work

- making sure that your actions at work do not harm the health and safety of other people

- what your employer must do to protect your health and safety at work

- what you should do if you believe that anyone's health or safety is being put at risk at work.

The book has been written in a way that makes health and safety issues easy to understand without going into too much detail about laws and regulations.

As you will see, the book is divided into 15 sections, each covering a different topic. The order in which the topics are covered is the same as the order of topics in the question book for the CITB-ConstructionSkills Health and Safety Test (Health and Safety Testing in Construction). This book is therefore an ideal revision guide for anyone preparing to sit the test.

Even if you are not sitting the test, you should find this book a useful source of information about health and safety on site. Its handy size means that you can carry it with you, in your pocket or toolbox, to refer to when you need it.

If you have any comments on the content of this book, particularly if you feel that there is extra information that should be included in future editions, please contact the writer, Denis Hands, on denis.hands@citb.co.uk or 01485 577625.

A message from the HSE

A competent workforce is needed to reduce accidents and ill health arising from work in the construction industry. The Health and Safety Test will help workers in construction to become competent at identifying health and safety risks on site. This Safe Start handbook provides a reference source for the Health and Safety Test as well as a stand alone guide.

Workers in construction need to participate in improving health and safety standards on site. By contributing to the consultation process with their employer and with principal contractors, workers can help to prevent dangerous conditions from developing on site. Workers in construction need to develop their skills in identifying risks and be confident in speaking out when they see something wrong.

01

General responsibilities

Construction sites can be dangerous places to work unless everyone plays a part in keeping health and safety under control. A lot of responsibility is put upon employers and main contractors to ensure that the workplace is a safe and healthy environment. Site managers are responsible for actually managing health and safety on site, but workers also have their part to play and you as a worker have your own health and safety responsibilities.

Health and safety law

The Health and Safety at Work Act puts legal duties on everyone at work including your employer and you as a worker.

Your employer must provide:

- a safe and healthy place for you to work
- tools, plant and equipment that are safe for you to use
- safe ways of working that avoid you being put at undue risk
- enough information, instruction, supervision and training to enable you to carry out your job without harming yourself or others.

As an employee you must:

- look after your own health and safety
- be careful that your actions do not put the health and safety of anyone else at risk
- use all equipment, tools, materials and substances safely and as instructed
- report anything on site that you think is unsafe, for example, a damaged ladder, or any safety rules that you think are not working
- follow any instructions that your employer gives you about health and safety, for example, not going anywhere on site that you are not allowed

- not interfere with anything provided for health and safety. For example, you should not let off a fire extinguisher as a joke or take down or deface a safety poster.

These points put a personal responsibility on you to behave in a safe manner whilst on site. Your personal responsibility is a very broad area and it is impossible to provide a detailed set of rules for every situation that you might be faced with at work. Your actions while at work will stem from your attitude to health and safety.

If you think that something on site is not safe, tell someone who can do something about it. By doing so, you might prevent an injury or save a life. If you are in a situation that is unsafe, you must stop work immediately and go to a safe place. Your employer should be supportive if you have to do this.

Health and safety regulations are also part of the law. They mainly apply to employers, although some regulations put legal duties on you as an employee. The way your employer manages health and safety on site should make sure that you are aware of any duties that apply to you, and that you comply with them.

You have a right to be consulted by your employer about health and safety issues, and to voice your concerns if you have any. Evidence shows that there are fewer incidents and accidents on sites where employees are actively involved in health and safety, for example by becoming health and safety representatives or attending health and safety committee meetings.

Communication

Good communication of health and safety information is essential to control risks and prevent accidents and ill health. Below are described several ways in which this communication might take place.

Your employer's health and safety policy

Reading your employer's health and safety policy will tell you how health and safety is managed in your company. It will tell you who is responsible for certain aspects of health and safety, how these responsibilities are carried out and what the arrangements are for specific matters such as first aid or accident reporting.

Site induction

It is important that you attend a site induction for each new site that you go to – you might not be able to work there if you don't. You will find that the induction talk covers many areas of site health and safety, such as:

- where the assembly point is if the site has to be evacuated

- who the first aiders are and how to recognise them

- where the site toilets and the canteen are

- any areas of the site that you cannot go to

- site rules on the use of some items of plant and equipment

- what to do if members of the public, including children, are found on the site.

It is important that you understand what is said during site induction. If there is something that you are not sure about, don't be afraid to ask the person giving the induction to explain it again.

Risk assessments

Your employer must make sure that you are aware of the risks to your health and safety that may arise from any job you are about to do, and also how these risks should be controlled or dealt with. This is achieved by carrying out a risk assessment.

A risk assessment identifies the **hazards** associated with a job. A **hazard** is anything that can harm your health or safety. Examples of hazards are:

* a power tool with an exposed blade such as a disc-cutter

* working at a height where a fall could cause you injury

* plant operating near to where people are working

* substances such as chemicals that can damage your breathing or skin.

By identifying hazards and eliminating the risk of anyone being harmed by them, a safe system of work will emerge. You **must** follow the safe system of work.

"It won't hit me – I've done a risk assessment."

Method statements

A method statement is written for some jobs. It explains how a job is to be carried out in a safe manner. Amongst other things it will identify the sequence of operations and any skills required. For example, if a mobile elevating work platform (MEWP) is to be used, a qualified operator will be required. The person who will supervise the job should also be identified in a method statement.

If you have to work to a method statement and are not sure about something in it that affects you, or if you cannot do the job in the way that the method statement says you should, stop work and report the problem to your supervisor or manager.

Toolbox talks

A toolbox talk is a short health and safety training session on a particular subject connected to the work being carried out at that time. A supervisor or manager usually gives toolbox talks at any time that it is possible to get everyone together.

A toolbox talk should give you the opportunity to ask questions about any part of the subject that you are not sure or happy about.

Permits to work

Permits to work are used for jobs that could be dangerous if the permit system was not used. A good example of this is work carried out in confined spaces. You **must not** start any job for which a permit to work is required until the 'start time' on the permit, otherwise you could be putting yourself in serious danger.

Conditions often found in permits to work are:

- what services must be isolated to allow the work to go ahead

- the limit of the work that is allowed under the permit

- what PPE (personal protective equipment) must be used

- what special safety precautions must be taken

- the date and time that the permit expires.

If a permit to work applies to a job that you are doing then you **must** comply with any conditions laid down in it. For example, if the job is not finished when the permit runs out, you and other people carrying out the job **must** leave the work area with everything left safe and report back to the person who issued the permit.

Site tidiness

Keeping your work area clean and tidy is an important part of working safely. You must make sure that waste materials are cleaned away and disposed of properly. Spilt liquids such as diesel oil and liquid waste such as paint or chemicals can be harmful to the environment if allowed to sink into the ground or if they get into a drain or stream.

If you are aware of any incident that might harm the environment you should let your supervisor know as soon as possible.

See Section 2, page 17 for further information on site tidiness.

The Health and Safety Executive

The Health and Safety Executive (HSE) is a government body that is responsible for overseeing most aspects of health and safety in the United Kingdom.

The HSE's main roles are to:

- offer advice on health and safety in relation to work issues

- visit workplaces to check that all necessary actions have been taken to ensure the health and safety of people working there

- visit workplaces to carry out investigations after a serious accident has occurred

- take enforcement action against anyone who has not given enough attention to health and safety.

Enforcement means taking one or more types of legal action. The HSE can:

- issue an Improvement Notice if it appears to an inspector that a health and safety law is being broken. The Improvement Notice will say how the law is being broken and give a date by which things must be put right

- issue a Prohibition Notice where something is so unsafe that all work connected with it must stop immediately and not start again until the matter has been put right. This could mean, for example, a power tool being put out of use until a guard is fitted, or even a whole site being closed down until major health and safety issues have been put right

- take employers and individual workers to court where serious breaches of health and safety law have taken place.

On most occasions the HSE inspector will just look round the site and only need to speak to the site manager. The fact that an HSE inspector is on site and speaks to you does not necessarily mean there is anything wrong and you need not do anything unless you are told to. You can always speak to an HSE inspector if you want to.

You don't need to behave any differently when an HSE inspector is visiting

02

Accident
prevention
and
reporting

Accident prevention

The nature of accidents

It is in everyone's interest to prevent accidents. Accidents are disruptive and have a negative effect on many people on site, not just the person who is hurt. Most accidents happen within the first few days of someone arriving on site.

The thing about accidents is that no one expects them to happen. If they did, actions would have been taken to stop them happening. Often, accidents happen because the health and safety rules have not been followed. Most accidents are easily preventable with a little care from everyone – both management and workers.

Falling from height has been the biggest cause of deaths on site for several years.

Common causes of accidents

Many accidents are caused by simple things like:

- untidiness, causing people to fall or trip

- hand tools, power tools and plant not being used properly

- poor manual handling

- personal protective equipment (PPE) not being worn when it should be

- sharp objects like nails being left lying around or sticking out of wood

- getting too close to where plant is operating

- people messing about.

Easy prevention

In the course of your work you can take simple actions to make sure that what you do will not cause an accident, either to yourself or to anyone else. These things include:

- following your employer's safe systems of work

- not taking short cuts that you think are a quicker or easier way to do something

- obeying all health and safety signs

- keeping your work area tidy, including the tools, equipment, and materials you use, and any waste material created by your work

- listening to and following any instructions that you are given during training such as site induction and toolbox talks

- following all of your site's health and safety rules

- reporting any work situation that you think may be unsafe to your supervisor.

"Look on the bright side – at least you were wearing a safety helmet."

The cost of accidents

The most obvious cost of an accident to you as a worker is time off work and a loss of wages. Other costs may not be so obvious to you, such as:

- permanent physical disability that stops you from ever coming back to work again, or from doing other things you enjoy like playing a sport

- the emotional stress of knowing that your actions contributed to an accident

- the stresses of being interviewed and also possibly appearing in court.

Accidents will also cost your employer in terms of lost production, damaged materials, accident investigation, fines, increased insurance costs and finding replacement workers.

Accident reporting

The accident book

All accidents, no matter how trivial, should be recorded in the site accident book and reported to your supervisor. This will enable your employer to comply with their legal duties, which include making sure that all accidents are properly recorded in the accident book, and serious accidents are reported to the Health and Safety Executive. If you have an accident:

1. Your employer or supervisor must be told as soon as possible after the accident has happened.

2. You must fill in the accident book. If you are unable to do so, a workmate or supervisor may do it for you.

The details that must be recorded are:

- the injured person's name, address and occupation

- the place where the accident happened

- the date and time of the accident

- how the accident happened

- the details of the person filling in the book.

The written details of all accidents must be treated as confidential. Whoever is in control of the accident book should remove and file away each entry as soon as it is complete.

Witnessing an accident

Even if you only saw the accident and are not injured, you may be involved in an investigation as a witness. If you saw what happened it is important to tell your supervisor or employer what you know. An investigation may only involve the people from your company, but if the accident is serious, someone from the Health and Safety Executive might be involved as well. Either way it is important that you are honest in telling anyone investigating the accident exactly what you saw.

Near misses

A near miss is an accident that nearly causes someone to suffer an injury. For example, if a scaffold coupling is accidentally knocked off a scaffold platform and nearly hits someone below.

It is important that you report all near misses because there are lessons that can be learnt from them. You should report a near miss even if it was not you that was nearly injured. The fact that someone was nearly injured shows there is a problem. By telling a supervisor about it, the problem can be put right to stop it happening again.

"Is that what we call a near miss?"

Illnesses and diseases

Your employer has to report some illnesses and diseases to the Health and Safety Executive, in the same way that some accidents have to be reported. Examples of illnesses and diseases that can arise from construction work and which must be reported to the Health and Safety Executive are:

- leptospirosis (Weil's Disease)

- some forms of cancer

- hand/arm vibration syndrome

- occupational dermatitis.

It is therefore important that you notify your employer if you think that you might be suffering from a reportable, work-related illness or disease.

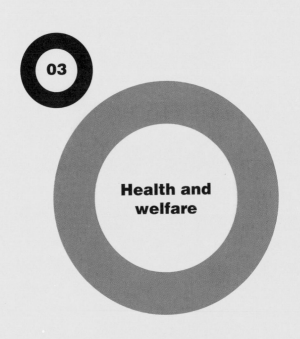

03

Health and welfare

Health

People who work in the construction industry are often well aware of the things they should do to work safely, but completely ignore any threats to their health. Ill health caused by work is called 'occupational ill health'.

At any one time there are more people off work because of occupational ill health than there are through on-site accidents.

Never forget the risks of working on a construction site

Work carried out on site could cause you health problems if:

- your employer has not identified the threats to your health which result from work, and developed methods of working that protect health

- your employer has not told you how you must work to protect your health

- you do not follow the methods of working that will protect your health.

The actions required to protect your health might be as simple as avoiding the manual handling of heavy loads or wearing the correct personal protective equipment (PPE) for the job in hand.

Many people who go off sick through occupational ill health never return to work or have to change careers.

The common causes of occupational ill health

Manual handling

The most common forms of occupational ill health in the construction industry are back injuries and other health problems caused by manual handling activities.

See Section 4, page 33 for information on manual handling.

Other forms of occupational ill health that could be caused by construction work are described below.

Skin conditions

Dermatitis is a skin condition generally caused by exposure to strong chemicals and other substances that irritate the skin. such as redness, itching or blistering. The hands and forearms are the most likely part of the body to be affected. You must avoid getting hazardous substances on your skin. If this is difficult, speak to your supervisor.

Allergic dermatitis can make your skin so sensitive to some substances that you may never be able to use them again. This could make it difficult or impossible for you to continue in your chosen job.

Using the correct type of work gloves or, in some circumstances, using barrier cream, will help protect your hands. However, often barrier creams will not protect you against stronger chemicals.

Dermatitis is often caused by the cleaning of dirty hands with strong spirits or solvents, such as thinners or white spirit, that take the protective oils out of the skin. You should use only soap or other skin cleansers and hot or warm water.

Between 5% and 10% of construction workers are affected by dermatitis caused by working with cement.

Skin cancer has not been taken seriously amongst the outdoor workforce of this country until recently. However, the number of skin cancer cases is increasing each year and you must protect yourself from exposure to the sun. You may think that a suntan looks good but it is a sign that your skin has already been damaged.

The people most at risk of developing skin cancers are those with fair or freckled skin and fair or red hair. However, everyone is at risk to one degree or another.

In hot weather wear loose fitting long-sleeved shirts and your safety helmet, which, besides its normal protection, will keep the sun off your head. You may also have to find a way of protecting the back of your neck, which is another vulnerable area.

If you notice changes to any moles that you may have anywhere on your body, seek medical advice as soon as possible.

Other cancers can be caused through skin contact with mineral oils, including those used in many items of mechanical plant. Continually leaving an oil-soaked cloth in a pocket of your overalls can be dangerous. The oil will soak though your clothes and affect your skin. Doing this for a long time can lead to a form of skin cancer.

Respiratory (breathing) diseases

Some of the materials used in the construction industry, such as solvents, adhesives, insulation materials and powders, can give off fumes, fibres or dust that can seriously damage your respiratory system (airways) if you breathe them in.

Some work processes such as grinding or cutting solid materials, and hot work such as burning off old paint, can also create harmful fumes and dust.

It is not only products that come out of a tin, packet or bottle that can harm you.

Respiratory illnesses such as asthma can be serious enough to end your working life. Other more dangerous substances, such as some gases or asbestos, may cause respiratory illnesses that can be fatal.

See Section 6, page 53 for more information on PPE and Section 8, page 73, on the safe use of hazardous substances.

Hearing problems

Noise at work and the health problems that come from it are particular problems in the construction industry.

See Section 14, page 122 for more information on noise at work.

Vibration

Prolonged exposure to excessive levels of vibration can cause serious health problems.

See Section 14, page 127 for more information on vibration.

Diseases carried in the blood

Leptospirosis (Weil's Disease) is caught when bacteria carried by rats get into your bloodstream. If you are working in or near water, or even on a waterlogged site, rats probably won't be too far away. Another form of leptospirosis is carried by dairy cattle, so those people who carry out building work on some farms are also at risk.

The way that the bacteria usually get into the bloodstream is through uncovered cuts and grazes on the skin, so it is best to keep these covered up with a waterproof plaster.

The problem with leptospirosis is that the early signs are like those for flu, but left untreated it can be fatal. If you start to suffer from what seems like flu but have reason to believe that it may be leptospirosis, see your doctor as a matter of some urgency.

It is wise to discourage rats from coming on to your site in the first place. One way that you can do this is by not leaving scraps of food lying around to attract them.

Legionella is a form of pneumonia caught from bacteria found in warm, damp places such as infected cooling towers, air conditioning systems and some parts of domestic hot water systems. People who work on these systems are most at risk. It is caught by breathing in water vapour contaminated with the Legionella bacteria.

If the presence of Legionella is suspected, employers need to devise systems of working that avoid workers inhaling contaminated water vapour. Employers should provide respiratory protective equipment where necessary.

Hepatitis is a blood-borne disease that can be caught from contact with infected needles and syringes. If you are working where people have been injecting drugs you may find discarded needles. If you find any drug-taking equipment during your work, leave it alone and let your supervisor know.

Tetanus is a disease of the nervous system caught from germs that usually get into your body through cuts or puncture wounds in your skin. The germs are often found in contaminated soil or manure on land that has been used as a garden or for growing crops. It is rare but it can be deadly. The most common early sign is an increasing difficulty in opening the mouth – this is why it's sometimes called 'lockjaw'.

Ingestion (swallowing) of hazardous substances

Ingestion means taking anything into your body through the mouth. This becomes a problem in the construction industry when harmful substances are not cleaned from the hands before eating or drinking.

You can avoid it becoming a problem by not letting harmful substances get onto your skin in the first place, for example by wearing work gloves that you take off before eating. Even if you wear work gloves you should still make sure that you wash your hands thoroughly before eating or drinking.

Drugs and alcohol

Neither drugs nor alcohol mix well with construction work – both can seriously affect the judgement of people who are under their influence.

Drugs

People who are under the influence of illegal drugs at work are a danger to themselves and everyone else on site. They are likely to suffer from:

- poor decision making

- slow reaction times

- clumsiness

- distorted vision.

It is likely that anyone caught working under the influence of drugs will have to leave the site immediately and will lose their job.

You should also be aware of the effects that some over-the-counter and prescription drugs can have if you take them. For example, some drugs that are prescribed by doctors for hay fever can make you drowsy, which is not a safe state to be in on a construction site.

If you are prescribed drugs by your doctor or if you have bought them from a pharmacy, you should check on any side effects that could affect your safety. You may need to discuss it with your supervisor and stay away from work if necessary.

Alcohol

Many people underestimate the length of time that it takes for the effects of drinking alcohol to wear off, particularly the day after a 'heavy session', when there may still be a lot of alcohol in the body. The usual after-effect of a heavy drinking session is a hangover, which will interfere with your decision-making and reaction times.

Besides being unsafe to themselves and others, anyone still under the influence of alcohol at work stands the chance of losing their job, and therefore losing money. Driving under the influence of alcohol is extremely dangerous and a driving ban can make life very difficult.

Drinking alcohol with lunch has virtually disappeared for those who work in construction. Don't be tempted but, if you are, don't go back on site afterwards because there will be a much higher chance that you have an accident.

Welfare

Your employer must ensure that adequate welfare facilities are provided on any site. This will include providing:

- toilets

- hand-washing facilities

- changing and drying rooms where necessary

- somewhere to take breaks from work and be able to heat up your own food

- a supply of clean drinking water.

Hand-washing facilities must include a supply of hot and cold (or warm) water, soap, and a way of drying your hands. These must not be used for washing off tools or boots. There should be separate facilities for doing this. Rooms in which you wash your hands must be well ventilated and lit.

The canteen, or whatever else is provided for breaks, must conform to certain standards:

- if food is prepared (except food that you prepare for yourself) it must be carried out to strict food hygiene rules

- there must be some way of boiling water

- there must be somewhere for non-smokers to be able to take their breaks without being bothered by tobacco smoke

- there must be suitable rest facilities for female workers who are pregnant and nursing mothers, where necessary.

All welfare facilities must be kept clean and in good order. If this is not the case, whoever is in charge of the site must be made aware of the problem.

Health and safety rules apply all the time you're on site, not just when you are working

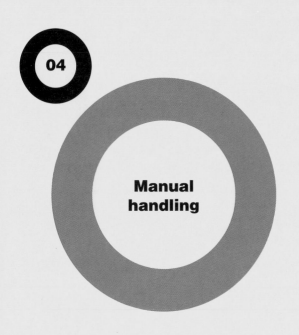

04

Manual handling

What is manual handling?

Manual handling is the moving of any load by hand. This includes for example, moving a load using a trolley or wheelbarrow. Even though it might be easier and safer to move a load that way, the trolley or wheelbarrow still has to be moved by hand. The only way to avoid manual handling is to move a load using mechanical handling equipment such as a crane, fork-lift truck or goods hoist. This is the safest option.

Generally, manual handling involves moving a load by:

- lifting
- pushing
- lowering
- pulling.
- carrying

What is the problem?

Manual handling is the biggest cause of occupational ill health in the construction industry. Injuries can be caused by carrying out the same manual handling operation again and again or even from one poorly thought out lift that could stop someone ever working again. Typical manual handling injuries include back strains, pulled muscles, torn ligaments and hernias.

In 2002, over 90,000 workers were injured by using poor manual handling techniques. Some were injured so seriously that they could never return to work.

There are also the injuries caused by the load itself, such as crushed fingers when putting it down or cuts from sharp edges.

Think before you try to lift a load

What can make a load dangerous to lift?

Most people think it is the size and weight of a load that makes it dangerous to move, and in many cases this is true. However, there are several other factors that you should consider.

- Shape, especially large items with no handholds – moving even a light load can give you problems if it is so large that you cannot see where you are going!

- Attempting to change your grip during the move – you may find yourself aching if you carry a large or awkward load over a long distance.

- If the centre of gravity is not in the middle or if it's an odd shape – liquids can slosh about, which changes the centre of gravity.

- The distance that you have to move a load – generally, the longer the distance, the lighter the load that you can safely move, unless you can put it down now and again.

- Whether the floor surface is uneven or sloping – you may have to consider whether you can safely carry some loads across a rutted surface or down a steep slope.

- Trying to lift a load in a small area – poor posture means that you can lift less weight.

- Lifting a load from the floor whilst twisting your body or in a seated position (or both!) – you will only be able to safely lift a lighter load than if you were standing.

- Lowering a load down from above head height – you will only be able to control a load that is lighter than if you were lifting it from the floor.

- If you have had a manual handling injury before, you may only be able to lift smaller and lighter loads. Make sure you tell your supervisor or employer about it.

Assessing the load

We all have different lifting capabilities based upon a lot of factors, such as our size, build, age and any manual handling training we may have received. Many people will recognise the loads that they have to lift and will be able to assess whether they are safe for them to lift simply by looking at them, for example a full bag of cement or a length of timber.

It becomes trickier when the weight of a load is unknown, in which case you may have to use other measures to assess whether or not you can safely lift it before trying. Heavy loads that are delivered to site may have their weight marked on them, or the weight may be found on the delivery note or manufacturer's information. By looking for information on the load or asking the right questions you will be able to find out the weight of most loads.

Think about safer ways of moving heavy loads

Can you break the load down into smaller parts?

The Health and Safety Executive (HSE) has issued guidelines saying that no one should be expected to lift blocks or kerbs that weigh more than 20kg.

If you are asked to move a load that is too heavy for you and it cannot be broken down or otherwise made safe, you must not try to move it. You must tell your supervisor or employer who will find a safe way of moving it by other means.

36

Your employer has a legal duty to make sure that you are not required to carry out any manual handling activity that will harm you. Using other methods to move loads is the best way to avoid manual handling injuries.

If it is not possible to avoid manually handling loads that might injure you, your employer must:

- carry out an assessment to determine the risk of injury

- devise a way of moving the load so that you are not injured

- tell you the safest method of moving the load.

As an employee, you must comply with any safe system of manually handling a load that your employer has told you about. However, if you think that there is a safer way of carrying out a manual handling activity, speak to a supervisor or manager about your idea. There may be a good reason why it cannot be done as you suggest, but sometimes the person doing the job knows a better, safer way to do it.

Solving the problem?

Measures that your employer might put in place as part of a safe system of manually handling loads could be:

- providing training on good manual handling techniques, such as **kinetic handling** which involves using the strong muscles of the thighs and legs rather than the back to lift loads

- providing equipment such as trolleys, pallet trucks or a set of rollers to make the moving of heavy and awkward loads easier

- making sure that you do not just go ahead with devising your own improvised way of moving heavy loads

- providing a lifting platform, such as a table, so that a lift can be carried out in two stages

- getting someone to lift a load with you (team handling). It is important that you are both about the same height and build, and one of you takes charge of the lift by giving the instructions

- putting newly delivered materials near to where they will be used to cut down on the distance that they have to be moved – avoiding 'double-handling'

- where possible, making sure that large loads are broken down into smaller, lighter loads

- making sure that loads which are not evenly balanced are carried with the heavy side towards the body.

Posture

A good posture (the way you position your body) is important when carrying out manual handling.

- FEET are placed hip width apart, with one foot slightly forward, in the direction of movement. This gives a good balance and provides a secure basis for the lift

- KNEES should be slightly bent

- BACK must be straight, although the body may be inclined forward

- ARMS should be as close in to the body as possible. The further the arms are extended the greater the strain. Elbows, too, should be kept close to the body

- GRIP must be firm and secure

- HEAD should be erect with the chin in.

Lifting a rectangular or square load

- Approach the load squarely, facing direction of travel
- Position feet approximately hip width apart, knees slightly bent
- Grasp load at mid-point nearest body using one hand, with the other hand grasp the furthest corner
- Pull load close to body, arms tucked in, keeping back straight
- Lift the load by smoothly straightening the legs
- Lean back slightly to counterbalance the weight of load before straightening up.

Personal protective equipment (PPE)

Safety footwear with steel toecaps will protect your feet if you drop a heavy or sharp load on them. Some manual handling jobs may also require that you protect your shins against injury.

Tough 'rigger' work gloves will protect your hands from being cut by the sharp edges of anything that you have to carry.

There are mixed views on back-support belts. They may help some people avoid back injury and the fact that wearing one will keep the muscles in the lower back warm is a benefit. However, Health and Safety Executive advice is that some people get no benefit from them at all and in some cases they may actually make things worse. It might be necessary for you to see your doctor or an occupational health specialist for advice.

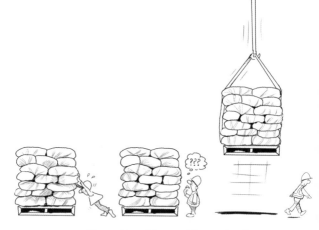

Manual handling problem solved!

Back pain

If you do suffer from back pain, advice from the HSE is:

- consult your doctor or an occupational health specialist
- keep as active as usual
- take simple pain relief tablets
- discuss with your employer or safety representative what can be done to stay at work

Do not:

- go to bed and wait for the pain to go away
- worry – back pain is not usually serious
- avoid activity to avoid pain – hurt does not always mean harm.

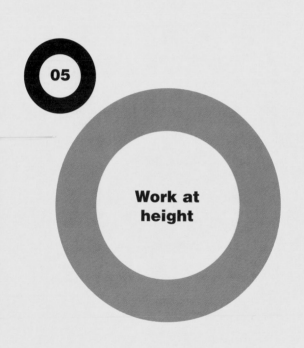

05

Work at
height

What is the problem?

Much of the work carried out in the construction industry is at height, which in many cases means working off a scaffold or mobile elevating work platform (MEWP).

Working at height is working in any place where a fall to a lower level could cause you injury, no matter how far you fall.

It is often said that most deaths and major injuries in the construction industry are a result of falls from height. This is true but you should remember that many of these falls are not from great heights. Deaths and injuries have resulted from people falling off low-level platforms, the back of lorries and even off the bottom few rungs of a ladder.

Whenever there is a need to work at height, your employer should try to find another way of doing it. The term 'working at height' can also mean getting to the place where you are going to work, for example crossing a roof or climbing a ladder. You should never be put in a position where you could be injured by falling. If you think that you have been asked to work where it is not safe, you must speak to your manager or supervisor.

Risk assessment

If you have to work at height because there's no other practical way of doing it, and where a fall could cause you injury, your employer must carry out a risk assessment and put systems in place to prevent you falling, or at least must make sure that you do not fall further than can be avoided and you are not injured if you do fall.

The risk assessment should look at all the factors that might make working at height unsafe, such as:

- difficult access to the place of work at height

- the effect of high winds, particularly if you are handling sheet materials

- poor weather, such as rain, sleet, snow or ice, making surfaces slippery

- how materials can be stored safely at height such as on a roof or high level floor slab.

In addition to any measures taken to prevent workers from falling, suitable steps must also be taken to prevent tools, equipment and materials from falling, in order to protect the safety of people working below.

Preventing falls

The safest systems of work are those that prevent people from falling. Steps commonly taken to prevent falls are things like:

- guard-rails on scaffold platform

- guard-rails around the deck or basket of a mobile elevating work platform (MEWP)

- catch-barriers at the eaves of a sloping roof

- restraint systems such as a harness and short lanyard to keep you away from the edge of a flat roof.

Whatever work you are doing at height you **must** use any safety equipment provided and follow any instructions you are given to make sure that your employer's safe system of work is effective.

Arresting falls

If it is not practical to put measures in place to stop you falling, there must be a safety system to keep to a minimum the height that you could fall and to make sure that you are not injured if you do fall. These are known as 'fall arrest systems' and there two main types:

- 'soft landing systems' such as safety nets, airbags or beanbags

- individual arrest systems such as a safety harness and lanyard.

Soft landing systems are generally preferred because they protect everybody working above them. If the safe system of work is well thought out, a soft landing system will limit the height of any fall.

If you have to use a harness and lanyard, you must be trained and competent to do so.

Other types of equipment, such as fall-arrest blocks, can be used with a safety harness. These allow free movement when the wearer is working normally but 'lock up' like a car seat-belt in the event of a sudden movement such as a fall.

A harness put on incorrectly or a lanyard not clipped to a strong point is not going to save any lives.

Roof work

Flat roofs

If you have to work on a flat roof that has no built-in edge protection, the safe system of work should:

- keep you away from the edge, or if that is not possible

- stop you from falling over the edge, or if that is not possible

- make sure you are not injured if you do fall.

Your employer should provide such measures as:

- edge protection, such as a system of temporary guard-rails that is secured against being knocked over

- barriers set well back from the edge to stop you getting too close to it

- restraining lanyards secured to a strong point away from the edge.

Sloping or 'pitched' roofs

Pitched roofs can be more of a safety problem, particularly when they have a steep slope. Anyone who stumbles or trips is likely to roll down the roof until stopped by something. Poor weather can also cause problems as the surface may become more slippery.

Safety measures that you may find in use when working on pitched roofs are:

- a working platform around a building at eaves height

- a catch-barrier at the eaves

- the proper use of roof ladders

- the use of soft landing systems.

Fragile roofs

Every year people are killed or seriously injured by falling through fragile roofs. Most fragile roofs are made from corrugated asbestos-cement sheeting and are easy to recognise, but there are other fragile materials used for roofing.

Even if the roof is made from a strong material it may have fragile rooflights that become difficult to see if they are dirty or covered with moss. It may be necessary to fit rooflights with secure, load-bearing covers whilst work is being carried out.

See page 151 for the warning sign that should be at all access points to a fragile roof.

If it is necessary for a worker to go on to a fragile roof, their weight must be spread across it. Crawling boards or other support systems will have to be used. Never try to cross a fragile roof by walking along the line of bolts used to secure roof sheeting to the T roof supports. It has been tried and often ends in someone's death.

Floor slabs

Floor slabs, particularly those in larger buildings, are often cast with holes in them to take lifts, staircases or services such as air-conditioning ductwork If the holes are not pre-cast, they will often be cut through the floor slab at a later date.

Any holes should be covered or guarded to prevent people from falling through them. If they are not, stay well away and tell your manager or supervisor.

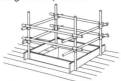

Guard-rails and toe-boards should be provided where necessary

Holes in roofs should be covered and clearly marked

46

Working over water

There are special rules if you are working at height over deep water. Your employer's safe system of work must consider such things as:

- measures to stop people actually falling or preventing them entering the water if they do

- the need for life jackets

- the rescue of anyone who falls in

- whether all workers must be able to swim

- whether or not anyone should be allowed to work alone

- workers contacting their supervisor at set intervals.

Access equipment

If you work at height you need a safe way of getting there and getting back down again. This can be anything from a simple piece of equipment like a ladder to a complex item of plant like a MEWP. The correct choice of access equipment can be crucial to the job being carried out safely.

Ladders

Ladders are easy to transport and are seen as a simple way of gaining access to height. However, many people fall from ladders because another type of access should have been used. A risk assessment by your employer would show whether it is safe to use a ladder or not.

To use a ladder safely you will need both of your hands free to climb it, so generally, carrying anything is ruled out. However, it is sometimes OK for lightweight, small items to be carried in one hand up a ladder.

You need three points of contact with a ladder at all times.

You will need a handhold at the point where you step off the ladder. This can be the ladder itself providing it extends at least five rungs above the stepping off point.

In most cases it will **not** be acceptable to use a ladder as a place of work. Only light work that will not take long should be carried out this way and one hand should always be used for holding on to the ladder.

To use a ladder safely, you must make sure that you follow the correct procedure:

* carry out a brief pre-use inspection and do not use it if damaged in any way

* tell your supervisor or employer if it is damaged and if possible put it where no-one else can use it

* rest it at the correct angle – the rule of 'one out for four up'

* make sure it is tied or lashed, preferably near the top, or footed by someone else

* footing a long ladder is useless and it's only any good on short ladders if the person has both feet on the bottom rung all the time

* use only on firm and level floor surfaces – ladders can easily become unstable

* always have one hand free to hold one of the stiles

* do not over-reach – come down and move the ladder

* do not rest it on flexible or fragile fittings such as plastic gutters

* only carry out light work of short duration from the ladder

* be careful about what items you carry up a ladder

* allow only one person on the ladder at a time

- do **not** use a wooden ladder that has been painted – the paint will hide defects

- do **not** use ladders near overhead cables – you risk electrocution

- keep the rungs free of mud if possible.

Don't take unnecessary risks when using a ladder

Stepladders

Stepladders should always be used with great care. Some sites won't allow them to be used at all. The common types of stepladder have four legs in contact with the ground. Therefore, they can only be used on a firm and level floor surface.

To use a stepladder safely, many of the safety factors for ladders will apply. Extra safety factors that apply to stepladders are:

- make sure that the restraining cords or struts are in good condition and fully extended

- make sure that the stepladder is positioned so that you face the work while you go up the stepladder. Having the stepladder 'side-on' so that you have to twist your body to work will make it unstable

- do not use the top third of the step ladder unless it is of a type designed to do so. These normally have a large base area and a top platform with a guard-rail around it.

Tower scaffolds

These days lightweight aluminium towers are often used for the type of jobs that at one time would have been carried out from ladders and temporary platforms. If you have to use a tower scaffold, remember that:

- they must only be erected or altered by a trained person
- guard-rails are often built-in but if not must be fitted where a fall from the platform would cause an injury
- they must only be used on firm level surfaces
- the wheel-brakes must be locked on when in use
- if necessary the tower must be levelled
- the working platform must be fully boarded
- the access hatch must be closed as soon as anyone using the tower is on the working platform
- the tower must not be moved while the working platform is occupied
- use only the built-in access ladder and climb it on the inside of the tower
- take down the tower if using it outside and high winds are expected.

Tube & fitting and system scaffolds

These are common on construction sites. They must only be erected, modified, and dismantled by competent scaffolders. Wherever a fall would cause an injury, guard-rails must be fitted. Toe-boards should also be fitted to prevent anything being accidentally kicked off the working platform.

Do not ever:

- remove a guard-rail, toe-board, tie or bracing. If it is in your way, speak to your employer or supervisor
- go on to a scaffold (or part of a scaffold) that has a 'Scaffold incomplete' sign on it (see page 148).

If you have to stack heavy materials on a working platform:

- you must **not** overload the scaffold

- brick-guards should be fitted if your materials will be stacked above the height of the toe-board

- they should be secured against accidental movement, for example in high winds

- they should not obstruct the safe passage of other people.

Lightweight staging and small mobile towers

These are replacing some of the less stable access equipment used in the past. You do not need to be a trained scaffolder to erect them but you must have had some training. Most of the rules for their safe use are the same as for other working platforms such as tower scaffolds.

Trestles need to be strong enough for the job and steady enough for you to work safely without creating a risk for anyone else. Do not remove any guard-rails, even if you think they are in the way. If the trestles are more than about a metre high, you might need to use a stepladder to get onto them.

Trestles are a safe way of working at height as long as they are used properly

Mobile elevating work platforms (MEWP)

Common types of MEWP are scissor lifts and cherry pickers. You will not be allowed to use these unless you have been trained and are competent. However, you may be a 'passenger' in one being operated by a qualified operator.

In most cases you will have to wear a safety harness and short lanyard to ensure that you cannot fall from the cage or platform. The free end of the lanyard will have to be clipped to a strong point on the machine fitted specifically for that purpose.

You must never jump or climb from the deck or basket of a MEWP onto a high structure. MEWPs are a way of working at height, and are not to be used instead of the stairs or a passenger lift.

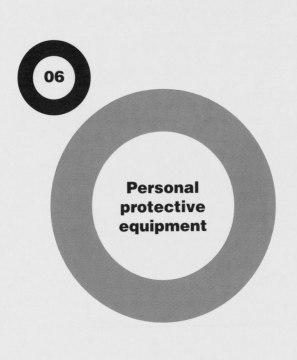

06

Personal
protective
equipment

What is personal protective equipment?

Personal protective equipment (PPE) is the equipment and, in some cases, clothing provided by your employer to protect you against threats to your health and safety whilst at work. PPE will often be issued on site after a risk assessment has identified the need to use them.

Common examples of PPE are:

- safety helmet

- safety boots

- eye goggles

- earplugs or muffs

- safety harness

- respirator.

Your employer **must** supply you with PPE whenever there is a hazard that can only be controlled by the use of it. It is therefore a 'last resort' method of controlling any risk.

Remember, a hazard is anything that can harm you.

PPE must always be supplied free of charge. Your employer is not allowed to charge you for it even if it is to replace PPE that has been damaged or that you have lost.

When should you wear PPE?

Some PPE, such as safety helmets, safety boots and high visibility clothing, is worn nearly all of the time at work. On most sites you can only take PPE off if you are in a safe area such as site offices or the canteen.

There are times when you may have to wear other types of PPE. The ways in which you will be made aware of this include:

- signs and notices, for example 'Hearing protection must be worn'

- instructions from your supervisor or employer

- from a risk assessment or method statement

- during site induction.

What are your responsibilities?

Your employer must provide PPE, but you, as an employee, have responsibilities as well. You must:

- take care of any PPE issued to you – this might mean visually inspecting it periodically and cleaning it where appropriate

- use your PPE as instructed by your supervisor or employer

- stop work and report to your supervisor if you have lost your PPE or if it is damaged

- do not work without it where it is required.

Head protection

On most sites safety helmets will be worn at all times except when you are in safe areas. They are worn to protect you against being injured by falling objects or banging your head.

To be effective, safety helmets must be worn the right way around (peak at the front) and should sit squarely on your head with the headband adjusted correctly. When your safety helmet could fall off, for example if you are leaning over a guard-rail or leading-edge, a chinstrap must be fitted and worn.

You must not damage the shell of your safety helmet in any way. Do not 'decorate' it or put unauthorised stickers on it. Chemicals in paint, marker pens and some glues can react with the plastic of the shell and reduce its strength.

Dropping your helmet from height on to a hard surface can also reduce the strength of the shell even if there is no obvious damage. If this happens you should change your helmet.

Foot protection

Safety boots must be worn at all times on site. A feature of safety boots made for wearing on construction sites is a steel toecap that prevents injuries to the toes. Some safety boots also have a steel plate embedded in the mid-sole to prevent puncture wounds to the bottom of the foot from upward-pointing sharp objects.

Where sites are wet or muddy and wellington boots are necessary, proper safety wellingtons must be worn.

Body protection

High visibility clothing and any other clothes provided by your employer to protect against weather conditions or workplace hazards are classed as PPE. Keeping your body and muscles warm will help prevent some types of injury.

Depending upon the type of work you do, protective clothing may be required to protect your body against:

* strong oil and chemicals

* fire hazards

* entanglement in moving parts of machinery

* rough surfaces.

Hearing protection

On most sites work activities will sometimes require hearing protection to be worn. The sign on page 124 will appear anywhere that hearing protection must be worn.

See Section 14, page 122 for more information on noise and how it can harm you.

The most common types of hearing protection used on site are earplugs (either disposable or reusable) and earmuffs. You may need training in how to effectively fit some types of earplug into your ears. If they appear loose or fall out you are not inserting them properly.

One problem that can result from wearing hearing protection is that you are generally less aware of what is going on around you, and may be more likely to miss shouted warnings. However, this must never stop you from wearing hearing protection when it is necessary to do so.

Always use the proper ear protection

Eye protection

You **must** wear suitable eye protection if there is any chance of suffering an eye injury through your work. See page 147 for the sign that will be displayed wherever you must wear eye protection, although there may also be other times when you decide that it is wise to wear it.

There are several types of eye protection available, each suitable for different types of work, for example:

- safety goggles

- safety spectacles

- full face shield.

Eye protection is made to protect the wearer against different hazards such as:

- flying debris
- chemical splashes
- airborne dust
- molten metal.

There is also specialist eye protection that is only used by certain trades, such as a welder's goggles.

It is essential that the eye protection you are given is suitable for the hazards you are likely to come up against.

Skin protection

Protection of the skin is probably the area of PPE that is most ignored. The hands and forearms are the most likely part of the body to be affected. Skin complaints such as dermatitis are easily prevented but are quite common in the construction industry.

Some substances can cause such severe dermatitis that sufferers have to give up their job.

Injuries such as cuts and abrasions caused by sharp objects are also easily prevented with a bit of care.

Where risk assessments show that you need to wear gloves, you must do so. Make sure that the substance you are handling does not get inside your gloves.

There are many types of work gloves available to protect the wearer against skin complaints that affect the hands. Examples of these are:

- chemical resistant

- abrasion resistant

- heat resistant.

If not carefully chosen, certain types of glove may make it more difficult to carry out work in which a degree of 'feel' is required. If you find that you cannot do your job properly, speak to your employer or supervisor – do not work without hand protection where it is needed.

Barrier cream will offer some protection to the skin but it may not be very good against some chemicals.

Fall arrest equipment

Fall arrest equipment such as a harness and lanyard is also PPE. If you have to use it you must be trained. There are several types of harness available and it is essential that you are supplied with the correct type.

The common types of harness are those used to:

* arrest the fall of someone who is working at height

* rescue casualties from confined spaces

* limit the range of movement of the wearer to keep them away from a place of danger. These are known as 'restraint harnesses' and are used with a short lanyard.

See also Section 5, page 44 for the safe use of harness and lanyard.

Flotation equipment

If you have to work above water or any other liquid where there is a risk of drowning, you should be provided with a buoyancy aid such as a life jacket. Some buoyancy aids will keep you afloat but may leave you face down if you are unconscious.

On the other hand, self-inflating life jackets will automatically inflate and turn you on to your back if you fall into water, keeping your face and airways clear of the water, even if you are unconscious.

Other, more basic but equally important PPE, such as life-buoys, life-rings or throwing lines may be provided when it is necessary to work above or near to water.

Respiratory protective equipment

There are many substances that are harmful to health if they are inhaled (breathed in). Some of these might be fairly obvious like the fumes given off by solvents or adhesives – there will probably be a warning on the tin.

However, the danger from some other harmful substances, like those created by a work process, may not be so obvious. For example, the fumes given off when burning off old paint or the dust created by cutting some materials like concrete or hardwood can be harmful to health.

In many cases, to prevent this harm it will be necessary for employers to provide the correct respiratory protective equipment (RPE).

Sometimes it's hard to tell whether fumes are harmful or not

Some examples of RPE are simple half-face
filtering face masks, half-face or full-face
respirators with replaceable filter cartridges
and even self-contained breathing apparatus.

Different types of RPE are effective against
different hazards so selecting the correct
choice of RPE is essential. For example,
some RPE that is effective against
dust particles (solids) will be useless at
protecting you against fumes (gases).

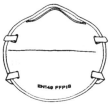

The type of RPE that is needed to carry
out any particular job will be determined
by assessing the risk.

Low quality RPE

If you are self employed and provide your own RPE, be cautious
of cheap half-face masks that can be bought from some DIY
shops and supermarkets. These are often not made to any
particular standard. The quality of their performance is not known
so they might not protect you from any respiratory hazards created
by your work. A nuisance dust mask may not protect you at all
from gas, fumes and even some types of dust.

All PPE is manufactured to European Standards. Do not use any
item of PPE that does not carry the letters 'BS EN' followed by
three or four numbers.

07

Emergency procedures and first aid

Site evacuation

On any site there should be plans for what to do if the site has to be quickly and safely evacuated (cleared) in an emergency, for example a major fire or a large chemical spillage. You must know:

- what the evacuation signal is

- whether the evacuation signal is tested

- if so, at what time the tests are carried out

- where the assembly point is (the place you have to go to)

- who you should report to at the assembly point.

This information should be given during site induction and should be displayed on health and safety notice boards on larger sites.

If you are not sure about any of the evacuation plans – ask!

If the evacuation signal is tested, it will usually be at the same time and on the same day of each week or month so that people know it is a test.

The sign on page 153 will tell you where to assemble if the site is evacuated.

If the emergency evacuation signal is sounded at any time other than when it is being tested you must:

- assume that it is the real thing

- stop whatever you are doing and leave everything in a safe state

- make your way to the assembly point by the quickest safe route

- report that you are there and not still on the site.

Do **not** just wander off without reporting to anybody. If the person in control has not accounted for you, it will be assumed that you are still on the site and lives may be put at risk looking for you.

Never go back on to the site until allowed to do so by a supervisor or manager.

Larger sites may have a special telephone number to call if you notice an emergency situation. If not, and you spot an emergency, call your supervisor or site manager.

Emergency escape routes

On larger sites, particularly where work is carried out on more than one level, the emergency escape routes may not always be obvious unless signs are displayed.

On some sites you may find that the emergency escape routes change as construction work progresses. What was an escape route last week might now be blocked off with a brick wall. An example of a 'no escape route' sign is on page 148.

Make sure that you always know where your escape routes are.

First aid

What is first aid?

The aim of first aid is to:

- reduce the effects of an injury or illness by giving immediate assistance to prevent the situation getting any worse **and**

- ensure that an ambulance or other professional medical help is on hand as soon as possible if required.

Accidents and injuries do happen on site and your employer must provide:

- enough first aid equipment, such as one or more first aid boxes

- trained people to respond to an incident, for example first aiders.

During site induction you should be told:

- what arrangements are made for first aid

- who the first aiders are

- how to contact or recognise them.

First aid equipment

You should always find at least one first aid box on any site, usually kept in the site office and containing basic first aid supplies such as plasters, bandages and sterile wipes. If what you need is not there or the first aid box is always empty, tell your supervisor or employer about it.

There should not be headache tablets or any other type of medicine in a first aid box.

On larger sites you may find a First Aid Centre with a site nurse and extra first aid equipment such as stretchers or emergency rescue equipment. You may also find that emergency showers are provided.

Workers who have to work alone or a long way from the site office may be provided with a small 'travelling first aid kit' that they carry with them.

Keep your travelling first aid kit safe and within easy reach

It is usual for the accident book to be located close to the office first aid box so that those who are being treated can record details of their accident in the book straight away.

See also Section 2, page 18 on accident reporting.

In situations where airborne dust may be a problem, whether through work activities or not, eyewash stations should be provided which will enable anyone to gently wash the dust out of the eyes of someone else. The location of eyewash stations will be indicated by the sign on page 153.

First aiders or other assistance

During site induction you should be told who the first aiders are or at least how to recognise them. On some sites first aiders are the only people wearing safety helmets of a particular colour (usually green). Sometimes they also have a 'First Aider' sticker on their safety helmet.

Make sure you recognise the site first aiders

Only qualified first aiders are allowed to carry out first aid. Anyone else trying to do so, no matter how well intentioned, might only make matters worse. Even first aiders are not allowed to give you any medicines unless they are authorised by someone who is medically qualified.

On larger sites there might be a full-time Site Nurse. On smaller sites there might only be what is called an 'Appointed Person' who is not a first aider but has been trained to:

* take charge of the first aid arrangements

* look after any first aid equipment or supplies

* call the emergency services and direct them to where they are needed.

Discovering a casualty

If you are the first on the scene at an accident your actions could be crucial, even if you are not a first aider.

The first thing you should do is make sure that you are not in any danger yourself.

There are other simple things that you could do to help someone who has been injured. Examples of these are:

* removing the hazard (the thing causing the danger) if it is possible and safe to do so

* where possible, turning off the electrical supply if someone is in contact with live electrical cables. Never attempt to grab them: you could also become a casualty

* sending for the first aider (or emergency services if there is no first aider on site). A mobile telephone could be useful

- not leaving the casualty on their own unless absolutely necessary, and offering comfort until help arrives

- running clean cold water across the eye of someone who has got dust or grit in it. Never poke around the eye with a handkerchief or anything else

  getting someone who has burnt their hand to plunge it into clean, cold water and leave it there until help arrives

If you are not a first aider, you should **not:**

- treat any injuries such as cuts, wounds or broken bones

- remove any objects from puncture wounds

- attempt to rescue anyone from a confined space, such as a sewer. Many people have tried and become casualties themselves

- move unconscious people unless you have to get them out of danger

- move anyone who has lost the feeling in any part of their body unless you have to get them out of danger

- try to immobilise any broken bones

- give food or drink to a casualty, or allow them to smoke

- give any medicine to a casualty.

Becoming a first aider

First aiders are all volunteers but they can really make a difference and that difference could be someone's life. If you'd like to become a first aider talk to your manager or supervisor about it.

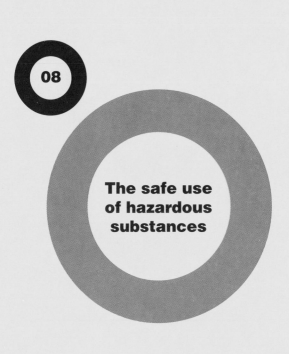

08

The safe use
of hazardous
substances

What exactly is a hazardous substance?

Many substances that are used in the construction industry could harm your health if the hazards are not properly controlled. These are not just materials or products that are bought from suppliers, such as cement, solvent cleaners, diesel fuel, adhesives or timber treatment products. They also include some of the substances that are created by work processes, such as the dusts and fumes caused by activities like cutting, grinding or welding.

Any hazardous substance, whether it's solid, liquid or gas, could cause you health problems and, in the worst cases, kill you.

What can they do to you?

The effects that some hazardous substances can have on your health are:

- immediate, for example burns to the skin caused by splashes of acids or chemicals

- long-term, like some forms of cancer caused by exposure to asbestos

- sensitising, which means that you would start having a serious reaction when you are in contact with less and less of the substance.

How do they get into your body?

Depending upon their state (for example solid, liquid or gas) they can get into your body in several ways:

- dusts, fumes and fibres are inhaled (breathed in). Your respiratory system can deal with a few of them but some fibres and dusts can get through your body's defences and into your lungs

- vapours are also breathed in and your body has no way of filtering them out of the air you inhale

- some harmful liquids can pass through cuts and grazes in your skin and some can even pass through unbroken skin

- if your hands become contaminated with a hazardous substance and you do not wash it off before eating, drinking or smoking, you might transfer it into your body through your mouth.

Of course, it might not be you using the hazardous substance that harms your health. Other workers might be using hazardous substances near you. If you think that your health might be put at risk by what someone else is doing, tell your employer or supervisor.

Your employer's legal duties

Your employer must take the necessary measures to ensure that your health is not harmed by exposure to any hazardous substance. The Control of Substances Hazardous to Health Regulations (COSHH) put legal duties on your employer to make sure that hazardous substances are used safely. The safest way to deal with hazardous substances is to replace them with less hazardous substances. If it is not possible to do this, methods of working that prevent the user being exposed to the harmful effects of the substance must be thought up – this is called your employer's safe system of work.

To assess the harmful effects of a substance your employer will:

- read the manufacturer's information on the substance

- make an assessment of the substance (the COSHH assessment), which means finding out how it can cause harm to your health and the precautions that must be taken to ensure that any possible harm is avoided

- make sure that **you know** how the substance can harm you and what you must do when using it to avoid harm. This usually involves your supervisor or employer explaining the COSHH assessment to you

- make sure that you follow any instructions given regarding the safe use of the substance.

Your responsibilities

For your part, you must:

- follow your employer's safe system of work, for example by correctly using any PPE and by following instructions

- tell your employer if you are not sure about something, for example, if you feel that the safe system of work is not effective.

Identifying hazardous substances

It is generally easy to tell if substances bought from a supplier are hazardous. They will have one of the following symbols on the container:

Symbol	Category	Effects
	Toxic or Very Toxic	Even small quantities can cause death or serious damage to health
	Harmful	Can harm your health
	Irritation	Can cause irritation to the skin or breathing passages
	Corrosive	Can cause burns to the skin and destroy body tissue

Some hazardous substances do not have a label that tells you what the hazards are. These are the hazardous substances that are created by work processes such as welding (fumes), cutting (dust) or painting (vapour).

Your employer must find out what hazardous substances might be created by the work that you do and then go through the same COSHH assessment process as for hazardous substances that are bought in.

There are some hazardous substances that do not come under the COSHH regulations, because they have their own special regulations, such as asbestos, lead or liquefied petroleum gas (LPG). These will not have the special symbols above on them, but your employer will still have to assess the risks involved in working with them.

If you find an unlabelled container with a substance in it, assume that it is hazardous, put it somewhere safe and let your supervisor or employer know.

Report any hazardous leaks to your supervisor

Asbestos

Asbestos is a particularly harmful substance that has killed many people. The danger comes from breathing in asbestos fibres which can form an invisible airborne dust. Breathing in asbestos fibres can lead to lung disease, cancer and death. There is no known cure for asbestos-related diseases.

There are three types of asbestos, commonly known as blue, brown and white. All are dangerous. Asbestos discolours over time or it might have been painted so its actual colour, if you discover it, may be totally different.

For many years asbestos was used widely in the construction industry and many buildings will still contain it. The use of asbestos is not allowed now apart from in a few specialist situations, so there should be no chance of exposure to asbestos in new builds. The danger lies where you are working on an existing building such as adding extensions, modification, refurbishing it or demolishing it.

Building owners should know where asbestos is located and be aware of the condition it is in. However, they might not, and if you think that you may have disturbed asbestos or a material containing asbestos, you should:

- stop work immediately
- warn others nearby to keep out of the area
- let your supervisor or employer know.

Typical areas where asbestos might be found are:

- the lagging of boilers, pipework or ducting
- sprayed coatings or fibrous lining of fire-resistant partitions
- sprayed coatings to ceilings, columns and beams

- some older suspended ceiling tiles
- linings to lift shafts
- asbestos-cement roofing sheets, water tanks and rainwater fittings
- soffit panels in older houses.

Where fibrous asbestos has been used in construction, for example, to lag pipes or behind the external cladding of a double-skinned building, its appearance should be fairly obvious. However, if it has been used in a solid form it may appear as a white powder when you disturb the material, for example by cutting or drilling into it.

If you think you might have found asbestos, stop what you are doing immediately.

Most work involving the removal of asbestos can only be carried out by specialist contractors. They will work in a screened-off area that other people must stay away from. As they remove asbestos you might find bagged-up waste stacked for disposal. It will be identified as asbestos waste by the label.

Do not interfere with asbestos waste.

Lead

Lead is another hazardous substance, although nowadays there are few trades, apart from plumbers, that will come into contact with it. It is a poison that can collect in the bone marrow and affect the body's ability to produce new blood cells.

The breathing in of lead fumes or dust is the most common route of entry into the body. Lead is dangerous when it is heated, such as flame-cutting material coated in lead-based paint, burning off old paint that contains lead, or the burning of new lead carried out by plumbers. However, the dry sanding of lead-based paint is also a hazard if the dust created can be breathed in.

If lead is being worked, particularly if dust or fumes are being created, stay well away if you are not involved in the job.

Highly flammable liquids

Many liquid substances used in the construction industry are highly flammable, which means that they can easily catch fire and burn fiercely if care is not taken. Thinners, solvents and some adhesives are examples of highly flammable liquids.

Highly flammable liquids (HFL) are identified by the symbol on page 150, either on the container or around storage areas.

If you have to use a HFL make sure that:

- there are no naked flames or other sources of heat or ignition

- only the amount for the job in hand is brought to where it is being used

- proper storage is arranged for the remainder (if any)

- the right fire extinguishers are available.

See also page 155 for a selection of the types of fire extinguisher.

Liquefied petroleum gas (LPG)

LPG is used extensively on construction sites, both in connection with the work of some trades and for general uses like the heating of site offices. On construction sites LPG is usually contained in relatively small portable cylinders.

LPG is heavier than air, so if there is a leak the gas will collect at the lowest point it can get to. This could be the bottom of an excavation or in drains and sewers. Such an accumulation can be extremely dangerous if it goes unnoticed and there is a source of ignition nearby.

However, LPG has a distinctive smell so if there is a leak someone should notice. Another sign that there is a leak is the formation of 'frost' around the area where it is escaping into the air, for example around the valve of a cylinder. If you think that there might be an LPG leak:

- if it is safe to do so, turn off the supply by closing the valve on the cylinder

- open doors and windows if appropriate and safe to do so

- warn others to evacuate and keep out of the area

- try to eliminate any sources of ignition (e.g. people smoking in an office)

- tell your manager or supervisor straight away.

Disposal of hazardous substances

Many hazardous substances can also cause damage to the environment. They can contaminate land, drains, sewers, streams and the air.

If you have been using a hazardous substance and have some left over that is not worth keeping, make sure that you dispose of it properly. Your company (or the site) should have a procedure for disposing of all hazardous waste and empty or part-full containers.

You must not dispose of hazardous waste by:

- mixing it with general waste

- letting liquid waste seep into the ground

- pouring liquid waste down drains

- burying or burning the waste material or its container.

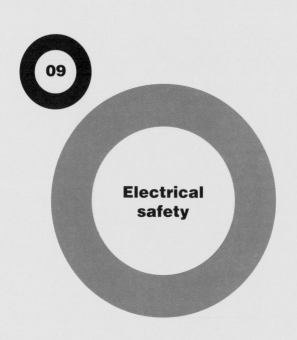

09

Electrical safety

What's the problem?

Electricity can be dangerous if it is not treated with respect. There is often no visible sign that an electrical cable is live, and mistakes can be fatal. The temporary nature of site electrical distribution systems and the possibility of them being damaged are more reason to be careful with electricity.

Switch the supply off if possible

Often you cannot be sure whether a cable is live or disconnected from the supply. If cables are hanging or lying near to where you are working tell your supervisor or employer about it, especially if the conductors (the metal bits in the cable that carry the electrical supply) are showing. You should never have to work where you are in danger from electric shock.

Never assume that the electricity supply is off

Electrical supplies are safest when they are switched off.

Sometimes the site electrics might not be what you want for your work. If you need an electrical supply and there is not one available, tell someone who can do something about it. You must not try to alter the site distribution system or run a temporary supply yourself.

Electrical hand tools

Hand tools used at work can be treated roughly, become damaged and therefore unsafe. Before using the tool each day, you should carry out a brief visual inspection of the:

* **casing** of the tool for cracks, burn marks, loose parts or other damage

* **plug** for cracks or other defects

* **cable** for cuts or wear, or looseness where it goes into the plug or tool.

Do not use any powered hand tools that are damaged. If an electrical hand tool stops working while you are using it, switch off the power and unplug it before trying to find out what is wrong with it. If it is obviously defective, put it where no one else can get at it. If tools are damaged they should either be repaired by a qualified electrician or replaced.

> **If electrical hand tools are damaged at all they are probably dangerous.**

If you have to adjust a hand tool, for example to fit a new drill bit to an electric drill, you should unplug it first. This could prevent you being injured if you accidentally touch the ON/OFF switch or trigger.

The voltage

Voltage is one of the main factors that determines how potentially dangerous an electrical supply can be. The supply that you have at home is 230 volt, often referred to as 'mains' voltage. If you touch a live 230 volt cable it will give you a severe electrical shock and could even kill you. This is why 230 volt tools are banned on most sites.

The tools used on site should run off a 110 volt supply, which, because of the way it is wired-up, means that the most severe shock you are likely to get is 55 volts. You would know that you had had an electrical shock if you touched one of these cables but it would not be severe and no lasting damage should be done to you.

There is a standard colour code for electrical equipment and at least part of 110 volt equipment will be yellow. The yellow parts may be:

* the casing
* the electrical supply lead
* the plug.

There are other standard colours for different voltages but you unlikely to have any involvement with these:

* blue – 230 volt supplies for outdoor use, for example a 230 volt output socket on a mobile generator
* red – 415 volt supplies used on equipment that takes a lot of electrical power such as tower cranes.

Battery powered tools

Battery powered tools are by far the safest things to use as far as electrical safety is concerned. Their low voltages give sufficient power for them to do their job whilst being very safe. Also, there is no trailing lead that people may trip over.

Using 230 volt equipment

It is usual for 230 volt equipment to be used in site offices and cabins. Kettles and office equipment are common examples. These can be just as dangerous as 230 volt hand tools if they are not looked after.

Some trades may also find that there is no 110 volt version of the specialist tools that they have to use on site.

Mains-powered equipment has a fuse in the plug. The fuse is a safety device that will 'blow' if something is wrong. All electrical equipment will have a correct rating for the fuse (for example 2 amp, 5 amp, 10 amp or 13 amp). The fuse is there to protect the equipment, not to protect you.

If the fuse blows in a tool that you are using:

* look for obvious damage
* if it is damaged, put the tool somewhere safe where no-one can get at it
* never replace a fuse with anything other than a proper fuse
* only replace the fuse with one of the same rating
* if the replacement fuse blows immediately, the tool is faulty and it should be put somewhere safe where no-one can get at it.

Because of the dangers from 230 volt tools they should always be used with a portable residual current device (RCD), commonly known as a 'Power Breaker'. These are plugged into the supply socket and the tool is then plugged into the RCD.

The purpose of an RCD is to cut off the supply very quickly if an electrical fault occurs. They should cut off the power before the fuse blows and before you or anyone else gets an electric shock. Using an RCD is good practice but not as safe as using 110 volt or battery powered tools.

The test button on the RCD should be operated daily to make sure that the device is working properly.

Extension cables

The use of extension cables is often necessary to get electrical power to where you need it. They can, however, be a danger to others. Because they tend to trail over long distances they can be a tripping hazard.

Run the cable above head height if this can be done safely. Where it must be run along the floor, it will usually be safest if the cable is run in the angle between the bottom of a wall and the floor.

If you have a long extension lead but only need a short length pulled out, you must decide whether it is safest to pull out the whole length, which may cause a tripping hazard, or to only pull off the drum the length you need and make sure that the cable does not heat up, which may cause a fire hazard. Ideally, you should get a shorter extension lead.

If you need to run an extension lead across an area where vehicles are operating, the cable will have to be protected. You should cover the part of the cable that will be crossed by vehicles with a proper cable ramp, which is usually made of rubber. 'Ramp ahead' signs should be displayed to warn vehicles approaching from all directions.

Do not cover the cable with something that just comes to hand, like a scaffold board. The cable will be damaged by the weight of vehicles crossing it.

Portable appliance testing

All 110 volt hand tools and associated equipment such as extension leads should be tested for electrical safety (known as PAT testing) by a qualified person at least every 3 months, or more frequently if the tool is subjected to particularly heavy use or rough treatment. All 230 volt equipment should be PAT tested at least every month. A 'PAT test' sticker that says when the next test is due will be put on the tool each time it is tested. How often electric tools are tested may vary from site to site.

Due to the low voltages used, battery powered tools do not need PAT testing, but the 230 volt battery chargers that go with them do.

The alternative to electrical hand tools

In areas where sparking from electrical hand tools could be a problem, for example in confined spaces with the possibility of flammable gases being present, or where water getting into hand tools could be a problem, it might be decided that electrical tools should not be used. Provision might be made for putting in a compressed air supply and pipework system to enable air-powered tools to be used.

Overhead cables

Overhead electrical cables crossing a site can be a problem. They usually carry a high voltage and are not insulated. Any contact with them usually results in very serious shocks and burns, or even death.

It is safest if the overhead supplies are switched off or re-routed during the construction work. Often this is not possible.

If work has to go on with the cables in place and still live, a system of barriers with signs and bunting should be put up by your employer or main contractor to stop anyone approaching too close to the cables. Goal posts with a 'crossbar' to indicate the maximum safe height should be erected wherever it is necessary for people and vehicles to pass under the cables.

Unless you operate plant the main danger to you will be if you get too close to overhead cables whilst carrying things like ladders (even wooden ladders), roof sheeting or scaffold poles. You can get an electric shock from equipment that is not metal if it is wet, because water on the surface will conduct electricity from the overhead cables to your hands. A safe system of work should make sure that you cannot get too close.

You do not have to touch an overhead cable to get a severe shock. Due to the very high voltages carried by some cables, the electricity can jump through the air (known as arcing) to any object that can conduct electricity and is close by. When this happens the electricity is carried by moisture in the air. The more moisture there is in the air, the further the electricity can jump.

Electricity and water don't mix

Buried electrical cables

See Section 15, page 135 for further information on buried electrical cables.

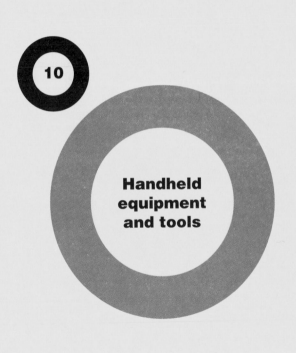

10

Handheld equipment and tools

Competence

Many types of hand tools are used by people in the construction industry. Besides the many power tools used on site, there are also non-powered hand tools such as handsaws, hammers, spades, trowels and pipe benders.

The importance of using power operated hand tools safely cannot be stressed too much. Rotating drill bits or saw blades, a jet of fluid at high pressure, or a hot air stream are all examples of the hazards that are present when some powered hand tools are used.

There also dangers involved in using non-powered hand tools. Many simple hand tools such as handsaws, trimming knives and even screwdrivers have blades that could do you serious harm if used incorrectly. A well maintained handsaw could cut through to the bone if your finger or thumb got in the way. A cross-head screwdriver could cause a serious puncture wound to your free hand if it slips off the head of a screw.

Your employer must not allow you to use any hand tool, whether powered or not, unless it is safe to use and you are trained and competent to do so.

Being competent to use any tool is a combination of:

- the **training** that you might need to be able to use certain tools safely

- **recognition** of that training

- your **experience** of using a particular tool (gained under supervision to start with).

The amount of **training** required for you to use any one hand tool depends upon the complexity of the tool, the techniques that must be developed for using it safely, and the potential seriousness of getting it wrong.

ognition of the training carried out is usually in the form of a
tificate issued by the training provider.

ur experience will come with time and actually using the tool.

etting it right

There are several things to think about before you use any hand
tool. Some of them are outlined below, but you may be able to
think of others:

- Does the tool need a brief pre-use visual inspection?
- If so, has it been carried out?
- If it is damaged, has it been put out of use?
- Is it the right tool for the job?
- Has it been properly maintained?
- Are all guards and other safety features in place and in
  working order?

Guards are used on many hand tools to protect the user, and
sometimes other people, from coming into contact with the moving
parts of a tool, or from bits of material that might be ejected at
high speed. Power tools should not be used if a guard is missing.

The guards should be adjusted to:

- allow you to see what you are doing
- expose only enough of the dangerous moving part to enable
  the job to be carried out, for example a blade.

When you finish using a power tool it should be allowed to run
down fully and stop before you put it down. Someone else, who
does not know that the tool has not yet stopped, could injure
themselves on the rotating blade or bit. Unplug the tool if you are
not going to use it again for a while.

Care should be taken with the use of devices that OFF' switch or trigger in the 'ON' position. If you for, have engaged it and put the tool down it will continu full speed.

You should make sure that any loose clothing and long secured in a way that will prevent it from getting caught moving parts of a power tool.

Do not attempt makeshift repairs to tools. Report any dama hand tools to your supervisor or manager so they can get the repaired professionally or replaced.

Petrol driven hand tools

Many of the bigger hand tools such as large disc-cutters and chainsaws will have petrol engines. Petrol must be stored in a safe way, and refuelling carried out in a safe manner:

- petrol must be kept in small quantities in approved containers

- refuelling should only take place in a safe, well ventilated area

- refuelling should not be carried out while parts of the tool are still hot

- a funnel should be used during refuelling to prevent spillage.

Exhaust fumes from petrol engines are toxic and must not be allowed to accumulate in confined spaces and other enclosed areas.

Electrical hand tools

All electrical hand tools used on site should be '110 volt tools'.
Before using any electrical hand tool you should carry out a brief
visual pre-use inspection of:

* power lead and plug
* casing.

Before you adjust any electrical hand tool you should take the
supply plug out of the electricity socket. This will prevent it causing
an injury if the 'ON/OFF' switch or trigger is accidentally operated
whilst you are changing, say, a drill bit or a blade.

*See also Section 9, page 85 for more information on the safe use
of electrical hand tools.*

Abrasive wheel machines

Disc-cutters are a common type of abrasive wheel machine used
on site. The abrasive wheel is a blade that rotates at high speed.
It is essential that as much of the blade as possible is covered with
a guard when the machine is in use. If an abrasive wheel can cut
metal or stone, it will cut through flesh and bone just as easily.

**The blade, rotating at high speed, makes the machine
very dangerous in untrained hands.**

Abrasive wheels wear while they are used and will have to be
changed regularly. The person who is responsible for changing (or
'mounting') the wheel must be trained and competent to do so as
it must be done correctly. This is not necessarily the same person
who uses the tool.

If an abrasive wheel is not mounted correctly it could become
unbalanced and break up (or 'burst') when it is rotating at high
speed, causing sharp fragments to be ejected and thrown over
a wide area. A guard would catch some of the fragments but
certainly not all of them.

'Over-speeding' can also cause abrasive wheels to burst. It happens when an abrasive wheel is fitted to a machine that can rotate it faster than it is designed to go. (All abrasive wheels have a maximum design speed.) A competent person will be able to check that an abrasive wheel and the machine are compatible.

Abrasive wheels should be used correctly

Cartridge operated tools

Cartridge operated tools work like a gun, by firing an explosive charge. They are mainly used to fire fixings into solid surfaces such as concrete.

These tools are very dangerous in untrained hands and you should not touch them unless you are trained and competent to do so.

Chainsaws

Chainsaws are not used very much during construction activities, but are sometimes used during site clearance before construction begins.

The main danger from chainsaws is that they have a totally exposed cutting chain. They can cause very serious injuries if not used properly by a competent person. Even then specialist personal protective equipment (PPE) must be worn to protect the user against accidental contact with the chain while it is running.

A major problem with chainsaws is 'kickback', which happens when the chain hits something buried in timber that it cannot cut through, for example a nail or screw. The chainsaw will uncontrollably kick upwards with the chain still running. Competent operators will be trained to deal safely with this and other hazardous situations.

Compressed air powered tools

Tools that are powered by compressed air are safer in some ways than, for example, electrical tools, because there is no chance of the operator getting an electric shock. However, as the air comes out of the tool, still under pressure, it can disturb debris and cause airborne dust and fragments.

High pressure air itself can be a hazard and cause accidental injection injuries to the skin if it is misused or if a leak develops in a supply hose. Never point an air hose at anybody. You could injure or even kill them.

Non-powered hand tools

Some of the safety requirements for even simple hand tools will be the same as they are for power tools. You must use the right tools for the job, visually inspected before use and maintained as necessary.

Check your tools before using them

Regular maintenance is particularly important where hand tools become damaged in normal use, for example chisels, drifts and other impact tools that are made to be struck by a hammer.

The head or end of the shaft on these tools will 'mushroom' and will need 'dressing' periodically. If they are not properly maintained fragments of metal will eventually break off the 'mushroom' and possibly cause injuries to the face or even become embedded in an eye if PPE is not being worn.

Dressing of the shaft will usually involve the use of a bench-mounted grinding machine and must only be carried out by someone who is competent to use it.

Other, non-powered hand tools have potentially dangerous features such as blades which must also be maintained in good order.

On some sites, you may be allowed to do very minor repairs to hand tools, but only when there are no safety issues involved.

Health considerations

See also Section 3, page 24 for more information on occupational health.

Many powered hand tools, such as a petrol-driven disc-cutter being used to cut concrete, will create dust, flying fragments or fumes. Breathing in this dust can create health problems. A high level of noise is also a problem.

You might need to wear PPE because of what someone else is doing.

It is possible to reduce the dust by using a machine that is fitted with either a dust collection system or a water spray that damps down dust as it is created. Similarly, where fumes are created by the work process, it is often possible to collect and pump them to a safe area using a mobile extractor.

Otherwise, it will be necessary for the operator to wear the correct PPE including high impact eye protection, respiratory protection and possibly hearing protection.

See also:

- *Section 6, page 54 for more information on PPE.*

- *Section 14, page 122 for more information on noise hazards.*

Hand/arm vibration can also be a problem when using many power tools that are either rotating (for example a disc-cutter) or percussive (for example a road breaker).

See also Section 14, page 127 for more information on hand/arm vibration.

Lasers are being used more often on site in tools such as levelling equipment. They use low power lasers that should not be a health hazard if the equipment is used properly. The laser beam often rotates so that it is impossible for anyone to look along the beam into the power source for more than an instant.

However, if static lasers (not rotating) are being used on site you must not allow the beam to settle on your eye. It is better to just stay out of the area if you can. If the laser is causing you a problem, don't just put up with it – go and tell a supervisor or manager.

If a high power laser is in use for any reason, warning signs like the one on page 151 will be erected and no one will be allowed into the danger area.

11

**Fire
prevention
and control**

The problem

The prevention of fire is very important on all construction sites. Every year major fires are caused, in the main, by carelessness. There are usually materials on site that can catch fire and burn if care is not taken. Anything that will burn is called **flammable**.

Elements of a fire

For a fire to start there must be:

- fuel, for example timber, paper and flammable liquids
- a source of heat such as a spark, welding torch or a cigarette that has not been put out
- oxygen in the air around us.

Ideally, the way to stop a fire from starting is to remove one of the above elements, although that may not always be possible because:

- materials that can burn will be present on most sites
- on most sites there will be sources of heat such as 'hot works', areas where smoking is allowed or even cooking in the canteen.
- there is nothing that we can do about the oxygen. It is in the air around us.

Practical control measures

The practical way of preventing fires from starting is to make sure that the fuel and a source of heat do not come together. Everyone on site can help to ensure that this does not happen.

There are several easy things that you can do, like:

keeping your work area tidy by getting rid of flammable waste material before it can build up

be careful if you use equipment that produces sparks or heat, such as welding or brazing equipment, boilers or hot air guns

using and storing highly flammable substances, such as liquefied petroleum gas (LPG), in a safe manner

complying with the site rules for fire safety such as using hot work permits and obeying the site smoking policy

being aware of the things that could cause a fire such as vehicle fuels not being stored safely or an LPG system showing signs of leakage, noticeable by a frost forming around the area of the leak

reporting to your supervisor or employer anything that you think might be a fire risk.

Hot work permits

Hot work permits are a way of controlling the risk of fire when a job will create sufficient heat to start one if care is not taken. Jobs like using a disc-cutter to cut metal, gas welding or using a hot-air gun or blowtorch, will often need a hot work permit.

The permit will specify certain conditions that must be complied with before, during and after the job is carried out. These conditions will include such things as:

the person doing the job must have a serviceable fire extinguisher of the correct type at the place the job is being carried out

the scope of the work allowed under the permit will be specified and must not be exceeded

- the time and day by which the job must be completed. This is usually at least one hour before the end of the working day so that any outbreak of fire could be detected

- a check of the work area by the person who has done the job, after it is completed, for signs of anything that could possibly cause a fire.

Control of fire

Discovering a fire

If you discover a fire your prompt actions could be crucial in restricting the damage caused and, more importantly, in reducing the number of injuries and possible deaths.

If you discover a fire the first thing you must do is raise the alarm.

During site induction you should be told what action to take if a fire breaks out. This should include details of how to sound the fire alarm (if there is one) or any other method of alerting people, such as shouting 'Fire, fire, fire!'.

A mobile phone could also come in useful for informing the site office and calling the emergency services. It is better that several people all dial 999 than no-one at all.

You should also be told during site induction where to go to if the site is evacuated – this is called the assembly point.

See also Section 7, page 66 for further details of emergency procedures.

Fighting a fire

Your response to the outbreak of a fire will depend on many things, for example:

* the site rules or company policy might state that you leave firefighting to the professionals and go immediately to the assembly point

* if you have been trained to use fire extinguishers you may be able to make your own decision about whether to try to fight a small fire

* the nature of whatever is on fire or being heated by it, for example a liquefied petroleum gas (LPG) cylinder in the fire, would require everyone to evacuate the area.

   No matter what you are allowed or choose to do, your actions must never put you or anyone else in danger.

If you do attempt to fight a fire you must:

* be aware that it could grow out of control and **you must always have at least one escape route available to you**

* know where the fire extinguishers are kept. This is known as the Fire Point and is indicated by the sign on page 149

* know the correct type of fire extinguisher to use.

Fire extinguishers

There are several different types of fire extinguisher. Each type contains a different substance and is suitable for tackling different types of fire.

Most fire extinguishers are now red, although you will see some that are silver. The way of telling different types of fire extinguisher apart is by a different colour used somewhere on the cylinder of the extinguisher, often a coloured band around the body. A water extinguisher will be completely red.

The chart on page 107 shows you what types of fire extinguisher should be used on different types of fire and, equally importantly, which fires some extinguishers must not be used on.

Different types of fire extinguisher put out fires in different ways.

- **Water** fire extinguishers put out a fire by the water cooling the burning material to below the temperature where it can burn.

- **Foam and dry powder** extinguishers smother the fire by keeping out the air, and starving it of oxygen.

- **Carbon dioxide** extinguishers displace and dilute the air around the fire with a gas that will not burn.

Chart 11.1: Types of portable fire extinguisher and what to use them on

Read the instructions on the fire extinguisher before using it.

Class	Substances, materials, etc.	Water (red)	Foam (cream)	Carbon dioxide (CO2) (black)	Dry powder (blue)
A	Carbonaceous and organic materials, wood, paper, rag, textile, cardboard, common plastics, laminates, foam	YES *Excellent*	YES	YES *Difficult to use outdoors in windy conditions For small fires only if no water available*	YES
B	Flammable liquids, petrol, oil, fats, adhesives, paint, varnish	NO	YES *If liquid is not flowing*	YES, *but not ideal*	YES
C	Flammable gas: LPG, butane, propane, methane, acetylene	YES *Will cool the area and put out secondary fires*	YES *If in liquid form*	YES	YES
D	Metal, molten metal, reactive metal powder	NO	NO	NO	YES *Trained person – if no explosive risk Special powders are available, but dry sand or earth may be used*
Electrical	Electrical installations, typewriters, VDUs, computers, photocopiers, televisions, etc.	NO	NO	YES	YES, *but not ideal Or switch off electricity and deal with as an ordinary fire*

Notes: Dry powder may not penetrate spaces or behind equipment
Light water foam (AFFF) may be used instead of water or foam

Using fire extinguishers can cause you harm if the wrong one is used or if they are not used correctly. These points will be covered during training on the use of fire extinguishers.

- When a carbon dioxide extinguisher is discharged the horn through which the gas passes gets very cold. If you hold the horn while you discharge the extinguisher, you are likely to get a severe 'cold burn' on your hand.

- The content of water and foam extinguishers will conduct electricity and you could be electrocuted if you use them on a fire involving or near to live electrical circuits.

- Using a water extinguisher on burning oil or fat will cause a violent reaction and spread the fire.

Do not be tempted to use fire extinguishers if you have not been trained.

Learn the different types of fire extinguisher before you need to use them

Ease of escape

In the event of a fire it is essential that everyone can quickly get to a place of safety.

Your work practices must not block off any fire escape route or make it difficult to get to firefighting equipment. For example, a small tower scaffold or a stack of materials could easily block off a corridor or staircase that is the only escape route for other people, or possibly prevent anyone getting to a Fire Point. You must speak to your supervisor or employer before you do something that will block the escape route.

Don't try to be a hero – it might only make things worse

12

Safety signs and signals

Safety signs

Safety signs are a common way of giving you and everyone else on site clear health and safety messages.

Safety signs are colour-coded so that you will easily be able to identify what a sign is telling you.

- Blue and white signs (a white image on a round blue background) are **mandatory signs**. These tell you something that you **must do**, for example wear hearing protection.

- Red and white signs (a red circle and diagonal line on a white background) are **prohibition signs**. These tell you things that **you must not do**, for example 'no entry on to scaffold'.

- Yellow and black signs (a black triangle and image on a yellow background) are **warning signs**. These warn you of a hazard or danger in the area you are in, for example 'fragile roof'.

- Green and white signs (white image on a square or oblong green background) are **safe condition signs**. These tell you about safe site areas and first aid, such as a first aid box, assembly point and fire exit signs.

Signs relating to fire equipment are also red and white but they are white images on a red background, and are usually square or oblong. These might be fire point signs, fire alarm signs and hose reel signs.

Some other signs that you may see will be orange and black. Generally, these are found on containers of hazardous substances and refer to the hazardous properties of the substance in the container. These signs might also be found around the storage areas for these substances. See page 76 for further information on these signs.

The colour appendix at the end of this book shows some of the signs you might see on site.

Safety signals

Safety signals are hand signals given by one person to direct the actions of another person, usually when they are operating plant or vehicles. Examples of safety signals are:

- a signaller or slinger giving signals to a tower crane driver during a lift

- a signaller or banksman directing the driver of a lorry that is reversing up to an excavation to tip materials.

Signallers and banksmen are trained and competent at what they do. If you are not trained do not get involved in giving signals to plant operators or vehicle drivers. You may be trying to help but there could be an accident if you get it wrong.

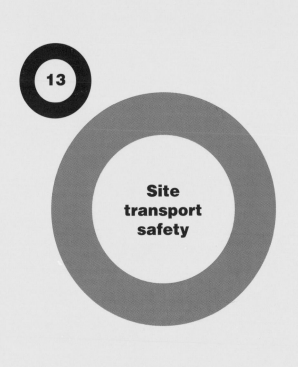

13

Site transport safety

Mobile plant

The movement and operation of vehicles and site plant causes many serious accidents on site each year. These accidents involve not only the driver or operator but also people on foot who may be working close at hand or only passing by.

Within this section all references to mobile plant and vehicles include any item of machinery or transport that can move either under its own power or by being towed. Common examples are:

- dumper trucks of any size
- mobile cranes of any type
- lorries
- mobile excavators of any type
- road rollers, including pedestrian operated rollers.

To simplify the wording of this section, the term 'mobile plant' will be used to cover all items of mobile plant and site vehicles.

The causes of accidents

Many accidents involving mobile plant happen because plant is large and the driver has a restricted view in at least one direction. Even though extra mirrors and on-board closed circuit television (CCTV) are sometimes fitted, drivers of mobile plant still often have at least one 'blind spot'.

With technological advances the driver's all-round vision should be improving but don't depend upon it. If you are on foot near to where plant is moving or operating, you could be at risk. It is far better to stay well out of the way if possible.

An item of plant does not have to be moving across the ground to be a danger to you. A mobile crane that is slewing, an excavator digging a hole or a lorry tipping materials, whilst not actually travelling, can still be a danger to people on foot who get too close.

Be aware of plant moving close to you

At the very least, a banksman or signaller should be directing the operation or movement of mobile plant in situations where other people could be at risk, such as when a lorry is reversing or when a crane is carrying out a lift.

Other accidents happen when people who are not trained or competent try to operate items of plant.

Do not attempt to operate any item of plant if you are not competent and authorised.

The chance of an accident between mobile plant and people on foot can increase after dark. Even with a high visibility jacket, if the lighting is poor you may be able to get too close to mobile plant without the driver realising you are there.

After dark and at other times when the light is not so good, remember that you will be more difficult to see.

Common types of accidents

Often the driver's field of vision is restricted to the rear. People have been seriously injured or killed when trying to pass too close behind mobile plant that is reversing.

Another common accident is when people are crushed between a fixed object, such as a wall, and the counterweight of a slewing mobile crane. As the crane slews, the gap between the counterweight and the fixed object suddenly becomes much smaller.

Stay out of the 'crush-zone'.

These types of accident happened simply because the people on foot did not keep clear of mobile plant. They may have been taking the shortest route to where they were going, but in the end, they did not make it.

The shortest route is often not the safest.

Site management of mobile plant

A well managed site will be organised to reduce the chance of accidents between mobile plant and people on foot. Measures will be taken like:

- separate routes for mobile plant and people on foot with barriers between them

- separate site entrance for vehicles and people on foot

- site speed limits

- one-way systems

- reversing banned or minimised by the use of turning areas

- amber beacons switched on if plant is operating (even if temporarily parked or not moving)

- a signaller or banksman controlling the movement of mobile plant

- ensuring that all lights are working on mobile plant that operates after dark or in poor visibility.

Whether you are a plant operator or not, the site rules on the safe operation of mobile plant should be explained to you during your site induction.

Your actions can make a difference

- If you cannot avoid passing close to mobile plant that is working, you will have to be patient and wait until:
  o it has finished the job and stopped moving or working
  o it has moved away altogether
  o the driver or banksman knows that you are there, the plant stops operating and you are signalled to go past.

- Stay out of plant compounds and other parking areas unless your work takes you there, in which case be alert to plant starting up and moving off, and keep out of its way.

- Do not ask for or accept rides on plant that is not designed to carry passengers. Deaths have been caused by unauthorised passengers clinging onto an item of plant then losing their grip and falling under the tracks or wheels.

- Always wear high visibility clothing.

- Report to your supervisor or employer any aspect of plant operations that you think is a danger. Examples of this are where mobile plant:
  o is operating too close to you for comfort
  o travels too fast and is a danger to other people
  o ignores one-way systems
  o uses routes that are only intended for people on foot.

Messing around isn't fun if someone gets hurt

There may be occasions when there isn't time to tell your supervisor or employer about a problem. If you think there is danger from mobile plant because of the way it is being operated, or perhaps it is defective, it might be best to warn the driver directly if it is safe for you to do so. You might also have to warn other people in the area.

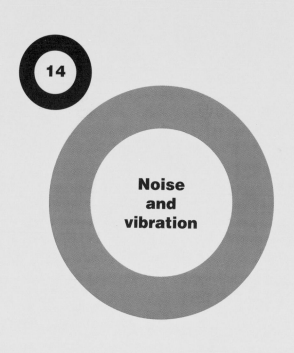

14

Noise and vibration

Noise: the problem

Many of the activities carried out during construction work can create noise levels that may damage the hearing of people on site, and even that of those further away.

Damage caused to your hearing by loud noise can be permanent and there is no cure.

Early signs that your hearing is being damaged are temporary deafness or a 'ringing in the ears' after exposure to loud noise. This can become permanent if exposure continues. If you have to ask people to repeat what they are saying to you when there is little or no noise you must take action to stop further damage to your hearing.

Permanent deafness will not only affect your life at work, it will also affect your quality of life at home and when you go out.

Hearing problems can affect your social life

The causes

Many things on site cause loud noise. For example, if you have to operate plant or powered hand tools there is a good chance that they will be noisy enough to damage your hearing if you do not take care.

Even if your work is not noisy, you may have to protect your hearing from other people working noisily near you. Some activities, such as driving sheet piles, can make so much noise that everyone on site might have to wear hearing protection.

Noise that can damage your hearing can be:

* continuous, for example from a diesel powered generator or using a power sander over long periods of time

or

* sudden peaks of high noise levels from impacts, for example, from a piling rig or a cartridge-operated tool being used near to you.

The effect of continuing noise on your hearing will depend on the level of noise and the length of time you are exposed to it.

The solution

Ideally, noise levels on site should be reduced to a level at which your hearing would not be at risk. However, this is often not practical. Your employer must therefore protect your hearing by issuing you with suitable personal protective equipment (PPE). Usually this will be earplugs or earmuffs. If these are correctly chosen by the person in your company who orders PPE, and are correctly worn by you, they will reduce the noise that you hear to a safe level.

See also Section 6, page 57 for more information on PPE for protecting your hearing.

Estimating the noise level

Taking accurate measurements of on site noise levels is a technical and complex issue, partly because noise levels go up and down during the day. There are, however, three 'rules of thumb' that can help you to decide whether or not you should be wearing hearing protection.

Rule 1

If you have to raise your voice to make someone who is only **one metre** away from you hear what you are saying, the noise level is so high that your hearing is at risk and you should **definitely be wearing hearing protection.**

Rule 2

If you have to raise your voice to make someone who is **two metres** away from you hear what you are saying, you should be thinking about putting your hearing protection on.

Rule 3

If in doubt, put your hearing protection on.

Always obey the hearing protection signs

Employer's duties

Your employer has a legal duty to ensure that your hearing is not damaged by exposure to noise while you are at work. Ideally, this will be achieved as far as possible by reducing noise levels on site so that noise is not a problem. Where this is not possible, your employer must make sure that you know:

- about the damage that loud noise can cause to your hearing

- what you must do to protect your hearing

- how and where you can get PPE that will protect your hearing

- your duties as an employee to protect your own hearing.

Practical control measures

The methods used on site to control the noise level might include:

- replacing noisy tools with similar equipment that is quieter, for example using an electric power tool rather than a petrol powered version

- using barriers to deflect or absorb the noise. This can be as simple as placing something like a diesel compressor behind a stack of materials, or using other site features to reduce workers' exposure to noise

- having plant and equipment serviced to keep it in good order and therefore make it less noisy. This will include ensuring that silencers, mufflers, and other features designed to reduce noise levels, are in place

- moving you away from the noise, or the noise away from you.

If, despite any measures taken, you are still exposed to noise levels that could damage your hearing, you must wear your hearing protection.

Any part of the site where the noise is loud enough to damage hearing must be designated as an **'ear protection zone'**. If you are working in an ear protection zone you **must** wear your hearing protection at all times until you leave it. The sign on page 124 tells you that you are about to enter an ear protection zone.

Employees' duties

You as an employee must:

- comply with employer's safe systems of work (like wearing your PPE in ear protection zones)

- look after the PPE issued to you by always keeping it in good working order

- get your PPE replaced if you lose it or it is damaged

- tell your employer if you think that work has damaged your hearing. You may have to go for hearing tests arranged by your employer. Don't leave it until it's too late.

The downside

If you are wearing hearing protection, you may be less aware of things going on around you, such as someone speaking to you or shouting warnings. Make sure you keep a good look out for what is happening around you.

Never use this as an excuse for not wearing hearing protection when you should.

Coping with deafness can cause loss of concentration, headaches, irritation, and fatigue, all of which could affect your ability to work safely.

Vibration: the problem

Serious health problems can occur from prolonged exposure to vibration of your hands and arms by using certain powered hand tools. This condition is known as Hand Arm Vibration Syndrome (HAVS).

Compressed air and electrical tools such as hammer drills, road breakers, disc-cutters and vibrating pokers all cause vibration either because:

- they are designed to vibrate in order to work, for example any tool with a 'hammer action'

or

- the way in which they are used, for example cutting hard substances with any type of hand held power-saw.

Generally, the longer you operate any tool that can harm you, the more likely you are to be harmed.

The early symptoms

Anyone who is in danger of suffering long-term health problems from hand/arm vibration will initially suffer from one or more of the early symptoms especially when conditions are cold and wet. These are:

- temporary loss of feeling in fingers

- tingling in the fingers

- whitening of the skin in the affected area (blanching).

The common name for health problems caused by vibration is **'vibration white finger'**.

The serious damage

If you start to experience the early symptoms of HAVS you **must** tell your supervisor or employer. If you ignore the early symptoms and continue to be exposed to harmful vibration, you are likely to cause damage to some or all of your blood vessels, nerves, muscle fibres, bones and joints in the affected hand or arm.

Damaged blood vessels will eventually affect the circulation in the hand and fingers, which can result in:

*   loss of dexterity, for example difficulty in handling coins or doing up buttons

*   a feeling of coldness in the affected area

*   losing sense of touch in the affected area

*   at worst, ulceration or gangrene possibly resulting in the loss of one or more fingers.

    At worst, the effects are disabling and permanent. Don't ignore the early symptoms.

The implications

The worst possible implications are:

*   you will suffer from a permanent disability

*   you could lose the ability to work at all or at least have to change your job

*   you might find that you cannot earn the amount of money you are used to.

The solutions

f you are at risk of suffering from hand/arm vibration because of he work you do, your employer must assess those risks and put in place measures to prevent it from happening.

The things that **your employer** can do are:

* look for other ways of doing the job, for example by using remotely controlled tools that are not held by the worker

* monitor how long tools that cause vibration are in use. Generally, this should be no longer than 2 hours for rotary tools and 30 minutes for impact tools.

* making sure that the hand tools which can cause vibration are well maintained

* replacing older tools with new tools that are designed to cause less vibration to the user

* making sure that any one person's exposure to hand/arm vibration is controlled by job rotation (sharing the job amongst several people)

* making sure that anyone at risk is told of how vibration can harm them and what they must do to protect themselves against it (a safe system of work).

The things that **you** can do are:

* follow any safe system of work developed by your employer, for example not using a tool for longer than you are allowed

* try to keep a relaxed posture whilst using vibrating hand tools. Your muscles will be less affected if they are not tensed. Where possible avoid using tools with your arms outstretched

* try to keep yourself warm and dry. Warm muscles are less likely to suffer. If your body or arms are wet it will be difficult to keep yourself warm

- Some gloves are designed to protect the wearer against the effects of hand-arm vibration. Whilst any gloves that keep your hands warm may be of benefit, some gloves are not totally effective in cutting out the damaging effects of this problem.

- let your employer or supervisor know if you think that you are suffering from any of the symptoms of HAVS.

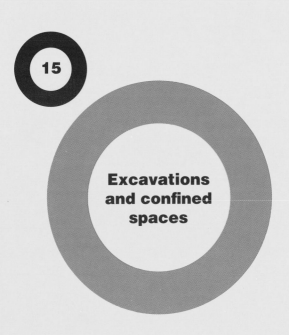

15

Excavations and confined spaces

Excavations

Generally speaking, an excavation is any hole or trench dug into the ground as part of construction work. Some excavations are no more than a couple of spades' depth and pose few health and safety problems. However, many excavations are deeper and are dug out by an excavator. They do not need to be very deep before becoming hazardous if care is not taken.

Falling material

Every year deaths and injuries occur when workers go into unsupported excavations, many quite shallow. The sides then collapse, trapping or completely burying the workers under the fallen soil and rock.

The fall of material into an excavation can happen through:

- the sides collapsing because they were not supported

- heavy vehicles getting too close and causing the sides to collapse

- spoil falling back into an excavation because it was piled too near to the top edge. ('Spoil' is the name for the soil and rock taken out of the ground while digging an excavation)

- the ground drying out and cracking or shrinking.

The fall of material into an excavation can be a result of deliberate actions such as:

- the tipping of materials by a vehicle such as a lorry or dumper

- filling-in of the excavation after work is complete.

The sides of any excavation that may collapse, causing someone to be injured, must be supported before anyone goes into it. Some methods of supporting the sides of an excavation, particularly long trenches, only support a short length of the trench at a time. If you have to work in an excavation that has only part of its length supported, for example when using 'drag boxes', you **must** stay in the protected area.

A cubic metre of ordinary soil weighs over a tonne. If you are trapped under it, you may never get out.

If anyone is buried by falling materials, rescue can only take place using very careful hand-digging to avoid further injury. It takes a long time for enough of the victim to be sufficiently uncovered to clear their airways, so they are less likely to be rescued alive.

Before any construction materials, for example concrete or gravel, are tipped into an excavation everyone must get out of the way or move to a safe area.

Poisonous gases and fumes

Poisonous gases and fumes that are heavier than air can collect in the bottom of excavations:

liquefied petroleum gas (LPG) or pipe-freezing sprays, which are used in some trades, can collect in areas like the bottom of excavations if allowed to leak

naturally occurring gases such as methane can seep out of the ground and collect in excavations

exhaust fumes from a petrol or diesel powered vehicle will collect in the bottom of an excavation if it is left with its engine running and exhaust close to the top of the excavation

fumes from solvents, such as those used for welding plastic pipes, will collect in low areas such as excavations.

It's not always easy detect the presence of gas in an excavation

Work must be planned to prevent the accidental build up of poisonous gases and fumes in the bottom of excavations. Sometimes fresh air needs to be pumped into the excavation.

If you are working in an excavation and can either smell gas or feel that you are being affected by it, for example feeling light-headed or dizzy, you must:

• warn others

• get out of the excavation immediately

• report it to your supervisor or employer.

Buried services

The types of services that are often found buried are:

- electricity cables

- gas mains and smaller gas pipes

- sewers and other drainage pipes

- water mains and smaller water pipes

- telecommunications cables including fibre optic links

- on industrial sites there may be compressed air, steam or oil pipes as well.

Accidental damage to most types of buried service might put at risk the health or safety of the workers actually carrying out the digging, particularly if a machine like an excavator is doing the digging. However, a major incident such as an explosion from a fractured gas main can injure people over a much wider area.

You must also consider the wellbeing of other people affected by the disruption of services, for example the loss of the electricity supply or telephone lines to a hospital.

You should never be put at risk of injury from accidental damage to buried services whether you are actually involved in digging excavations, working in them or working near by. Planning and investigations should find out whether there are any buried services before digging starts.

Although mechanical excavators are often used to remove most of the spoil, the final location and exposure of the buried service must be carefully carried out by hand-digging 'trial holes'.

It's possible that some buried services will not be shown on any plan. If the job is well planned, these should be found by a competent person surveying the area with a location device before digging starts. However, if you find an unexpected buried or underground service, you must immediately report it to whoever is in charge of the job. If the service has been damaged it is safest to warn others and for all of you to get out of the excavation.

The route of some buried services will be identified by a run of plastic marker tape or tiles that are buried above the buried service itself. If you discover anything like this when digging then, unless you were expecting to find it, stop digging and speak to your supervisor straight away.

Contaminated ground

Before carrying out any disturbance of the ground, such as digging an excavation, it will be necessary for whoever is planning the job to take into account what the land has been used for in the past. Previous development may have left the ground contaminated by, for example, industrial waste, hazardous chemicals or asbestos fibres.

If you notice strange smells coming from newly disturbed ground, you should inform your supervisor or employer immediately.

Responsibilities

Your employer must:

- make sure that the sides of excavations are supported if a fall of material is possible and would cause injury

- arrange for the excavation to be inspected by an authorised person at the start of every shift and on other occasions

- make sure that records of inspections are made and kept safe

- develop safe systems of working in and around the excavation

- provide a safe way of getting into and out of the excavation

- make sure that guard-rails and toe-boards are fitted around the top of the excavation where anyone who falls into it could be injured

- provide lighting around the top where it would be dangerous not to do so.

You must:

- follow any safe system of work specified by your employer

- wear any personal protective equipment (PPE) that may be necessary

- use the proper means of getting in and out. Do **not** climb up the side supports or use buried services that cross the excavation as foot-holds

- report to your employer or supervisor anything that you consider to be unsafe.

Confined spaces

The term 'confined space' refers to any area in which you have to work where your health or safety could be put at risk because of a lack of natural ventilation combined with:

- a reduced level of oxygen in the air: we need oxygen to live

- the presence of poisonous gases or fumes that will displace the oxygen

- the presence of flammable gases that create a risk of fire or explosion.

Confined spaces are usually thought of as totally enclosed work areas such as underground chambers or tanks. However, a confined space need not be totally enclosed, for example, LPG collecting in the bottom of an excavation makes it a confined space.

Common examples of confined spaces found or created during construction work are sewers, large enclosed tanks, service tunnels, deep pits and excavations. Other work areas that might not at first be thought of as confined spaces are basement rooms, boiler rooms, toilets and voids within buildings. An oil storage tank or water tank above the ground is also a confined space.

Make sure you know how to get out of an excavation or confined space

Reduced oxygen level

The oxygen in a confined space can be reduced by such things as:

- 'hot works' type of jobs during which combustion burns up oxygen

- the formation of rust on the inside of metal tanks will use up the oxygen

- people breathing consumes oxygen.

   As the oxygen level starts to drop you will become confused and lack coordination. If it drops further you could become unconscious and die.

The presence of poisonous gases

The presence of poisonous gases that replace oxygen can be caused by such things as:

- people breathing out carbon dioxide

- stirring up sludge or slurry in the bottom of an excavation

- rotting vegetation producing methane

- chemical processes, such as the breaking down of sewage, forming hydrogen sulphide, which smells like bad eggs

- rainwater filtering through chalk rock, which can cause carbon dioxide to be formed.

The presence of flammable gases

If a heavier-than-air gas such as LPG leaks, it will sink to the lowest point it can reach and may collect in the bottom of a confined space, forming a highly flammable atmosphere.

Methane, which is a naturally occurring flammable gas, can seep up from the ground into some confined spaces in which the walls are not lined, such as deep excavations. Stirring up rotting vegetable matter in the bottom of a confined space can also release methane.

Working safely in a confined space

The hazards outlined above show that work in confined spaces must be properly planned and carried out.

Training is needed for working in confined spaces. If you have not been trained, do not enter one.

Whoever is planning the job for your employer will have to carry out a risk assessment to establish any dangers present in the confined space. A method statement outlining the order of tasks necessary to complete the job safely will often support the risk assessment. A permit to work system might also be used to ensure that the job cannot start, or must not continue, until strict safety conditions are complied with. Typical conditions of a permit to work are:

- the time limit on completing the job – if the job is not going to be finished on time, the people doing it must make everything safe then leave the confined space before the permit runs out

- strict limitation of what work can be carried out under the permit – never go beyond the scope of what you are authorised to do

- a need to monitor the atmosphere before entry and continuously during the job

- the type of respiratory protective equipment (RPE) that must be worn

- the skills and training that might be needed, for example being trained to use some types of RPE such as self-contained breathing apparatus.

Other features of safe working in confined spaces are:

- having a rescue plan and a trained rescue team available. There should be no entry to confined spaces if these are not in place

- monitoring the air in the confined space before anyone enters and continuously whilst people are working in it, by using an air quality monitor

- the presence of at least one person at the entry to the confined space, usually referred to as the 'top man' whose job is to get the rescue plan under way if things go wrong and to generally relay information between the people in the confined space and those outside

- the actions to take if the alarm on the monitor sounds. This will be either to put on RPE, if you have it, or to get out quickly.

Improvised rescue

If you are outside a confined space and see someone in it in distress or who has collapsed, never attempt to rescue them unless you are part of a trained rescue team.

Many workers who have attempted to rescue workmates from a confined space have been overcome by the gas and fumes and have also collapsed or died.

Glossary

Many words and terms that you will hear on a construction site are explained in the main part of this book. The list below includes some more terms you might come across.

adhesive: a substance used for sticking things together
abrasive wheel machine: a machine, such as a bench-mounted grinder or a disc-cutter, which is used for cutting or grinding materials
allergy: a damaging reaction of the body caused by contact with a particular substance
asbestos: a naturally occurring, heat-resistant substance that was once used extensively in construction work. Breathing in asbestos particles is harmful to the lungs
asthma: an illness that causes difficulty in breathing
bacteria: germs that can cause some illnesses
barrier cream: a protective cream applied to your hands before starting work
bracing: scaffold poles that make a scaffold rigid
brazing equipment: used for heating and joining metal
brick-guard: a metal mesh fitted to a scaffold to prevent anything from falling through the gaps between the guard-rails and toe-board
bunting: a length of rope or wire to which small coloured flags are attached to attract the attention of people nearby
cable ramp: a temporary 'hump' laid over a trailing cable to protect it from damage by people or traffic passing over it
catch-barriers: a framework of scaffold poles and scaffold boards erected around a sloping roof to stop anything falling over the edge
CCTV: closed circuit television
cherry picker: a type of MEWP on which a passenger-carrying basket is located on the end of an articulating or extending arm
corrugated: ridged sheet material such as roofing sheets
COSHH: Control of Substances Hazardous to Health Regulations
crawling boards: a working platform or staging that allows access on a fragile roof

crush injuries: injuries caused by something crushing a part of the body

distribution system (electrical): the method that is used to get electrical supplies to where they are needed on site

double-handling: having to move something twice

employee: someone who works for someone else

employer: someone who has people working for him or her

European Standards: a standard of quality to which an item of equipment must be made and tested

HAVS: hand-arm vibration syndrome

Health and Safety at Work Act: the main piece of health and safety law

hernia: an injury that can be caused by poor manual handling techniques

HFL: highly flammable liquids

HSE: Health and Safety Executive

HSE inspector: an official who can inspect the site and take action if work is not being carried out safely

lanyard: a length of fabric that connects a safety harness with a fixed strong-point

ligament: a band of tough body tissue that connects bones or cartilage

LPG: liquefied petroleum gas

MEWP: mobile elevating work platform

PAT: portable appliance testing

PPE: personal protective equipment

purlins: metal or wooden spars that support a roof surface

RCD: residual current device

RPE: respiratory protective equipment

scissor lift: a type of MEWP with a platform that rises vertically

slewing: a part of an item of plant, such as the jib and counter-weight of a crane, rotating about a vertical axis

smooth technology (tools): modern hand tools that have been designed to vibrate as little as possible

soffit panels: panels spanning the distance between the edge of a roof and the walls of the building

solvent: chemical used to dissolve or dilute other substances

tripping hazard: items lying around that you might trip over

ventilated: supplied with fresh air

'SAFE START' – TRAINING RECORD

Name of company _____

Name of employee _____

The employee and supervisor should sign each area of training
listed below as it is completed. The manager responsible should
endorse the record and ensure that a copy is retained on file.

		Employee's signature	Supervisor's signature	Date completed
1	GENERAL RESPONSIBILITIES	_____	_____	_____
2	ACCIDENT PREVENTION AND REPORTING	_____	_____	_____
3	HEALTH AND WELFARE	_____	_____	_____
4	MANUAL HANDLING	_____	_____	_____
5	WORK AT HEIGHT	_____	_____	_____
6	PERSONAL PROTECTIVE EQUIPMENT	_____	_____	_____
7	EMERGENCY PROCEDURES AND FIRST AID	_____	_____	_____
8	SAFE USE OF HAZARDOUS SUBSTANCES	_____	_____	_____
9	ELECTRICAL SAFETY	_____	_____	_____
10	HANDHELD EQUIPMENT AND TOOLS	_____	_____	_____
11	FIRE PREVENTION AND CONTROL	_____	_____	_____
12	SAFETY SIGNS AND SIGNALS	_____	_____	_____
13	SITE TRANSPORT SAFETY	_____	_____	_____
14	NOISE AND VIBRATION	_____	_____	_____
15	EXCAVATIONS AND CONFINED SPACES	_____	_____	_____

I confirm that the above named person has completed training in
the subject areas listed.

Signed _____ Position_____

Signs and signals

Mandatory signs

Look out!

Wear a safety harness

Wear a hard hat

Wear eye protection

Wear work boots

Wear safety gloves

Prohibition signs

No pedestrians

No smoking

No escape route

Children must
not play on
this site

Scaffolding
incomplete
Do not use

Fire fighting equipment signs

Hose reel

Call point

Warning signs

General warning

Forklifts at work

Flammable

Explosive

Corrosive

Toxic

Danger of electrocution

Fragile roof

Radioactive

Laser beams

Confined space
No unauthorised entry

Danger
Men working overhead

Danger
Falling objects

Danger
Asbestos removal in progress

Warning
Stand clear of suspended loads

Caution
Trip hazard

Safe condition signs

Assembly point

First aid

Wash your hands

Emergency eye wash

Emergency shower

Signs on hazardous substances

HARMFUL

IRRITANT

HAZARDOUS TO
THE ENVIRONMENT

TOXIC

Types of fire extinguishers

Water

Foam

Carbon dioxide

Dry powder

Hand signals

Knowing these signals will help you to be aware of any dangers. However, you must not signal to plant operators unless you have been trained to do so.

Start

Stop

Danger: emergency stop

Left

Right

Raise

Lower

Move backwards

Move forwards

Jib up

Jib down

Extend jib

Retract jib

End

Stocksigns